All About Reading

Word Patterns

by

Lillian Lieberman

Illustrated by

Marilynn G. Barr

Publisher: Roberta Suid
Production: Little Acorn & Associates, Inc.

WORD PATTERNS

For a complete catalog, write to the address below:
Monday Morning Books, Inc.
PO Box 1134
Inverness, CA 94937

Call our toll-free number: 1-800-255-6049
E-mail us at: MMBooks@aol.com
Visit our Web site:
http://www.mondaymorningbooks.com

ISBN 1-57612-177-1

Printed in the United States of America
9 8 7 6 5 4 3 2 1

Contents

Introduction

All About Reading: Word Patterns is a book of worksheets, activities, and games for children in grades 1-3. The book is designed to reinforce word patterns that are essential to decoding words. It focuses on learning the six syllable patterns that make up many words. It covers short and long vowel words, the vowel-consonant-e pattern, r-controlled words, vowel team, and consonant + le syllable patterns. By learning and applying these patterns in reading, children can become skilled decoders.

The activities in the book reinforce and strengthen sound symbol association and word patterns with simple format and logical sequence of skills. Each instructive page begins with a brief explanation of the word pattern with several word examples. A variety of activities engage the children in learning. Children cut and paste, circle, color, and write. Catchy titles and related themes motivate and guide the children through the tasks. Bold print is used to emphasize the word patterns and important concepts.

Games culminate the activities for each particular word pattern. The children will enjoy the games using game boards, spinners, die, cards, or a BINGO set up. The games give the children a chance to practice skills in a fun and social setting and can be repeated for continuing reinforcement. The games are easy to use and make.

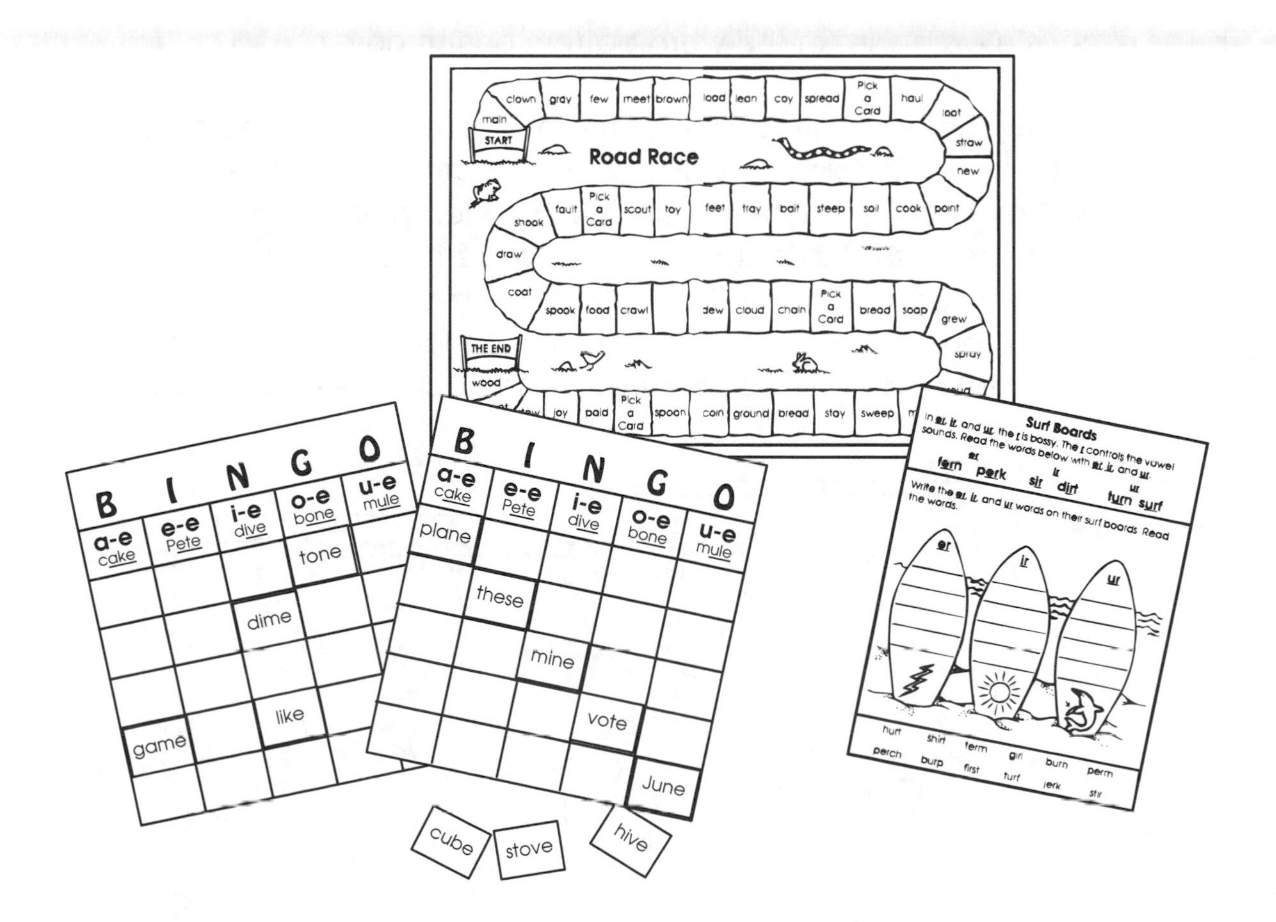

How to Use

Go over the concepts and word patterns beforehand so the children understand and feel comfortable with the tasks. Write examples on the chalkboard and point out the patterns. Have children identify them by underlining or circling the patterns. Make word cards and have children sort out the words to the different patterns. Help the children apply the word patterns in their regular classroom reading assignments. Encourage them to focus on the patterns as they work out words.

The activities in the book may be used to supplement the classroom reading program or become a core part of the reading program. The activities may be adapted for use in learning centers or in the special resource room.

How to Make

Worksheets: Duplicate each worksheet for the child to work on with guidance. Worksheets for each word pattern can be made into books for later review or reference or to take home to share. Staple a colored sheet of paper on each set of worksheets to make a cover. The children may cut out words from magazines that have the word pattern and paste it on the cover. Or they may use colored crayons or pencils to write examples of the word pattern on the cover.

Games: Follow the directions on the game pages. Duplicate and glue the pages onto the file folder or oak tag as instructed. Trim where necessary. Color and laminate if desired. Watch for specific directions on the game pages to duplicate more than once or to provide markers, a die, or other supplies. For file folder games, store loose game parts in a clasp envelope. Glue envelope on the back of the file folder. For **Final e BINGO** and **Apples on the Tree**, store each game in a clasp envelope.

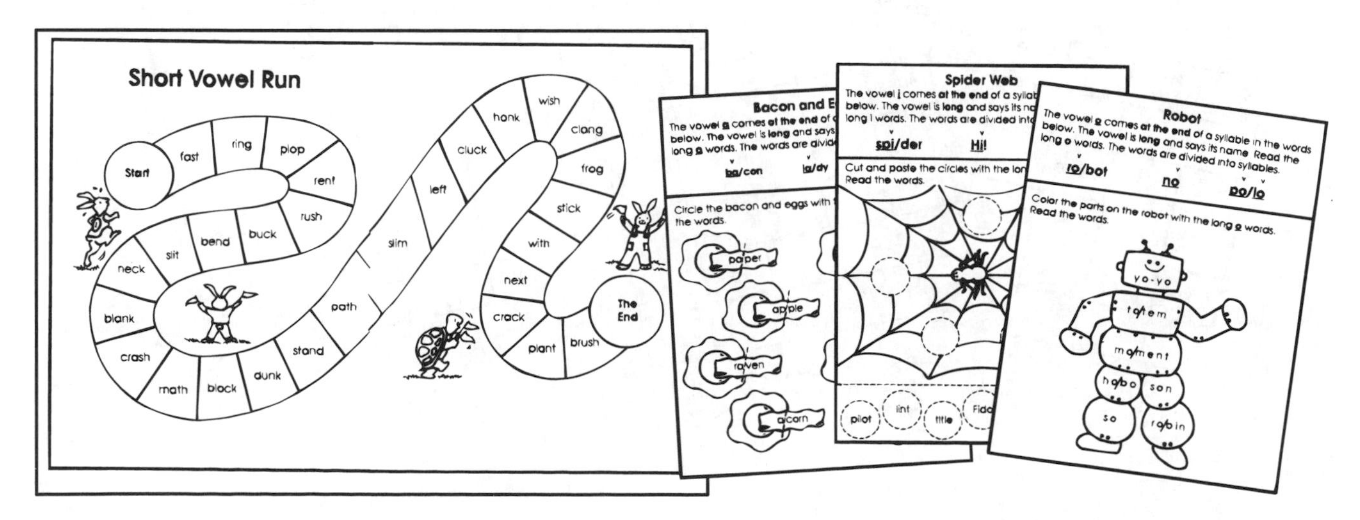

Enrichment

I Spy: (Short Vowel Patterns) On a large sheet of oak tag, write short vowel words with a felt pen. Write words that end with one, two, or three consonants after one vowel, i.e. mat, lost, lunch. Add three or four words that do not follow the pattern, i.e. free, team, etc. On a green, blue and red felt pen tape a piece of masking tape. Number the pens, 1, 2, or 3 to stand for the number of consonants at the end of the words. Tell children that when a word ends with one or more consonants after one vowel, the vowel is short. Ask the children to look for words with the pattern. Have them raise their hand and say, "I spy a word with two consonants at the end after a vowel. It says ____." Have the child come up and point to the word. If correct, the child can circle the word with the matching numbered pen. Continue in this manner until all the short vowel words are identified.

Long Vowel Bank: (Long Vowel Pattern) Make a bank out of a shoe box. On index cards, write long vowel words that have a single vowel at the end of the word or syllable, i.e. music, lady, spider, no, etc. Underline the part or syllable for easy identification. Write three to four words with other patterns for discrimination purposes. Place one word card on each child's desk face down. At a signal, let children take a peek at their word card. If they have a word card with a long vowel pattern, they raise their hands. In turn, they may read their words and identify the part that is long. If correct, they may put their card in the **Long Vowel Bank**. Children with other word pattern cards may not bank their cards. Shuffle the cards and use again.

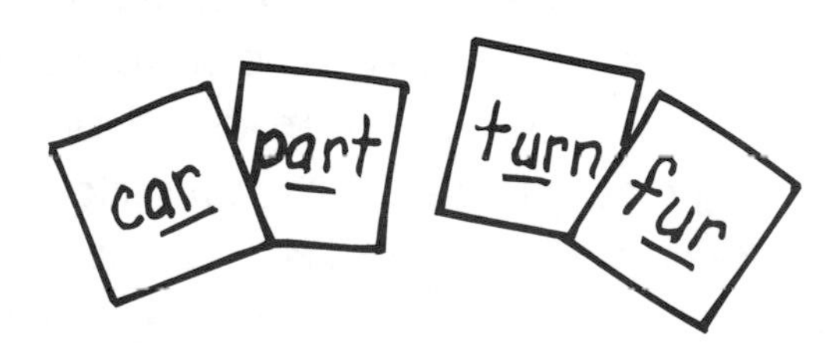

Crazy R Words: (R-controlled Pattern) On index cards, write r-controlled word cards, using **ar**, **ir**, **er**, **ur**, **or**. Make a pair for each r-controlled pattern. Make 10 cards in a set for two players. Make more sets for larger groups of players. Shuffle the cards. To play, deal out four cards to each child. Each child checks to see if there are pairs in their hand, such as two **ar** word cards. If so, the pair can be made into a book. Players then ask each other if they have a particular r -controlled pattern, "Do you have **er** as in f**er**n?" If so, player being asked must give up that card. If not, the first player takes another card from the pile. Players must read their Crazy R words each time. First player to get rid of all his/her cards is the winner.

Take a Card: (Final e Pattern) On index cards, write words with final e, such as lake, cube, time. Make a pair for each vowel-consonant-e pattern. Place the cards face down in playing area in rows. Play like Concentration. Players pick up two cards at a time to see if they match by vowel-consonant-e pattern. i.e. cake, name. Player reads the words. If they match, the cards are kept to make a book. If not a match, the cards are replaced. Players must show the cards before placing them back. The player with the most books at the end is the winner.

Puzzle Time: (Consonant + le Pattern) Write words with the consonant + le pattern, i.e. fid<u>dle</u>, ap<u>ple</u>, etc. Cut the cards just before the consonant + le pattern, i.e. puz/zle. Mix the word parts. Store in a clasp envelope or plastic zip lock bag. To use, have children take 4 word parts and try to make consonant + le words. On next turns, each child takes one more part. Players may trade parts by not taking an additional word part. Player with the most consonant + le words wins.

Vowel Team Bingo: Make blank BINGO playing cards for each player. Write vowel team words on small index cards. On a BINGO blank, write double vowel teams, such as **ai**, **ee**, etc. Double up with vowel teams on the extra spaces. Copy on colored construction paper, one for each player. Players cut their vowel team squares apart and place them in random order on their blank BINGO card. Place the word cards in a pile face down. Each player in turn takes a word card, reads the word, and turns over the matching vowel team square to the blank side on their playing card. Player loses turn if there are no more matches. First player to make a BINGO is the winner.

Bulletin Board

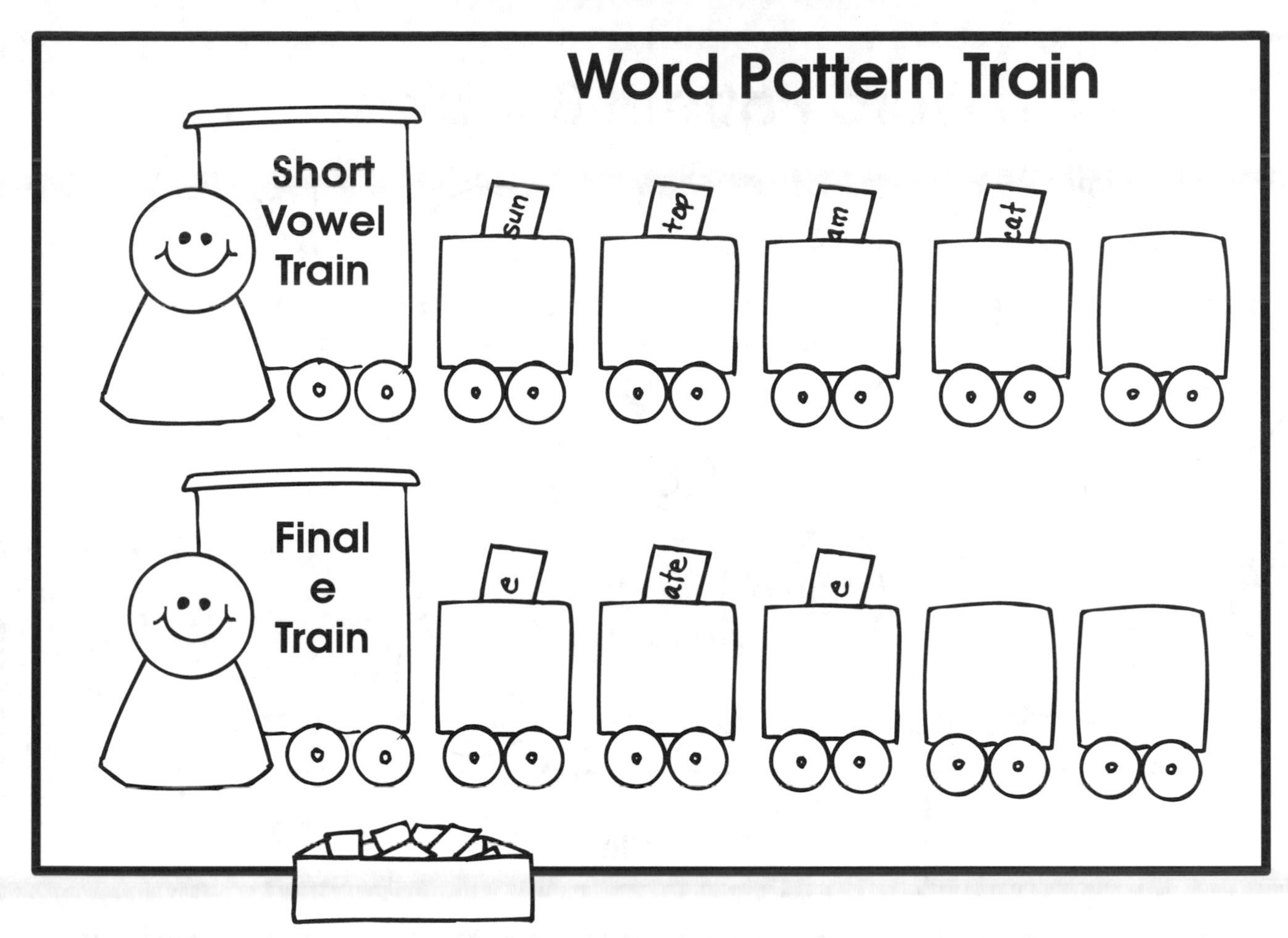

Word Pattern Trains: Use this bulletin board for different word pattern trains. Two or three of the word patterns can be set up for sorting out words that fit each word pattern train.

Materials: Bulletin board letters, bulletin board pins, construction paper, oak tag, felt pen, stapler, small index cards, yarn, shoe box.

How to Make: Pin bulletin board letters for the title, **Word Pattern Trains**. Cut out a train engine car from yellow construction paper for each word pattern targeted. Pin the engine to the left side of the bulletin board under the title. On strips of oak tag, write one word pattern with felt pen, i.e. **Short Vowel Train**, **Final e Train**, or **Long Vowel Train**. Pin one on each engine. Cut out six to ten train cars out of different colored construction paper for each train. Pin or staple them across in a row after the engine. Pin or staple only the sides and bottom edge of the cars, keeping the tops open for word cards. Pin short pieces of yarn to connect trains. Write ten or more words that fit each pattern on index cards with felt pen. Place cards in a shoe box nearby.

How to Use: Have a child take a word card, read it, and identify the word pattern. If correct, have the child place the card in a car box for that word pattern. If incorrect, the child puts the word card back in the shoe box. Continue in this manner until each car has a word card. The teacher or children check each other. To use for other word patterns, change the title on each engine car and make new word pattern cards.

Bulletin Board

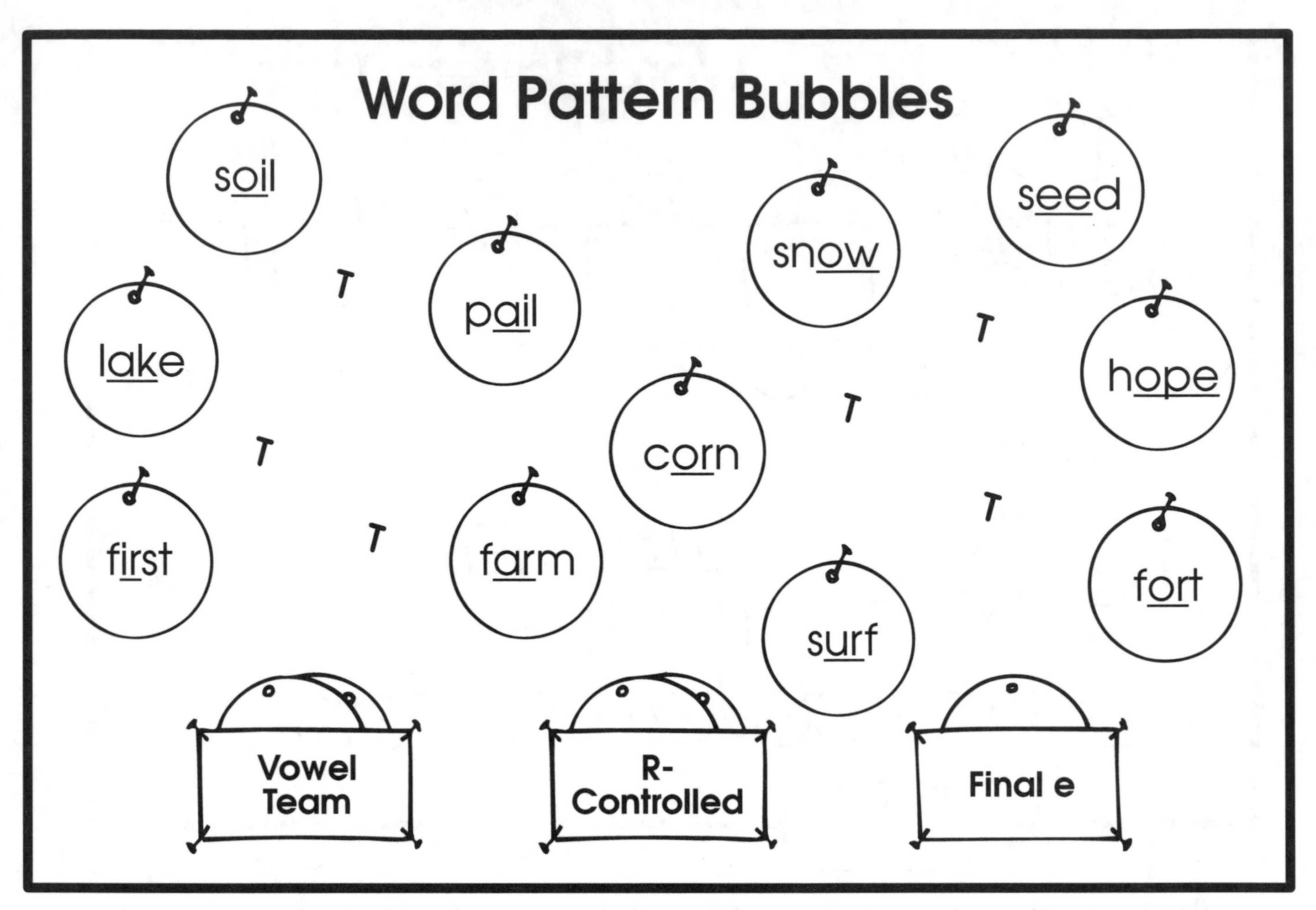

Word Pattern Bubbles

Materials: Bulletin board letters, bulletin board pins, scissors, colored construction paper, felt pen, stapler, hole punch, soft nerf ball or soft beanbag, letter-size envelopes.

How to Make: Pin bulletin board letters for the title. Cut out saucer-size round circles for the bubbles from colored construction paper. Punch a hole at the top of each circle. With felt pen, write a word on each circle, underlining the word pattern. Place pins randomly on the bulletin board. Slip each circle over a pin. Words may be confined to two or three different word patterns. For a more advanced class, more word patterns may be targeted. For each word pattern targeted, label an envelope with the word pattern with felt pen. Cut off the flap of the envelope and staple or pin to the bottom of the bulletin board, leaving the tops open.

How to Use: Have children in turn, throw the nerf ball or soft beanbag at the word pattern bubbles. If a child hits one of the bubbles, the child reads the word and identifies the word pattern. If correct, child places the bubble in the correct word pattern envelope. Continue in this manner until all bubbles are removed. Replace bubbles after all have been read and identified. To keep interest alive, change the word circles from time to time, or add another word pattern.

Make a Hit!

The words below end with **one consonant** after **one vowel**. The vowel is short. Read the words.

vc	v c	v c	v c
bat	**hum**	**pen**	**fog**

Cut out the baseballs with the short vowel pattern. Paste them on the bats. Read the words.

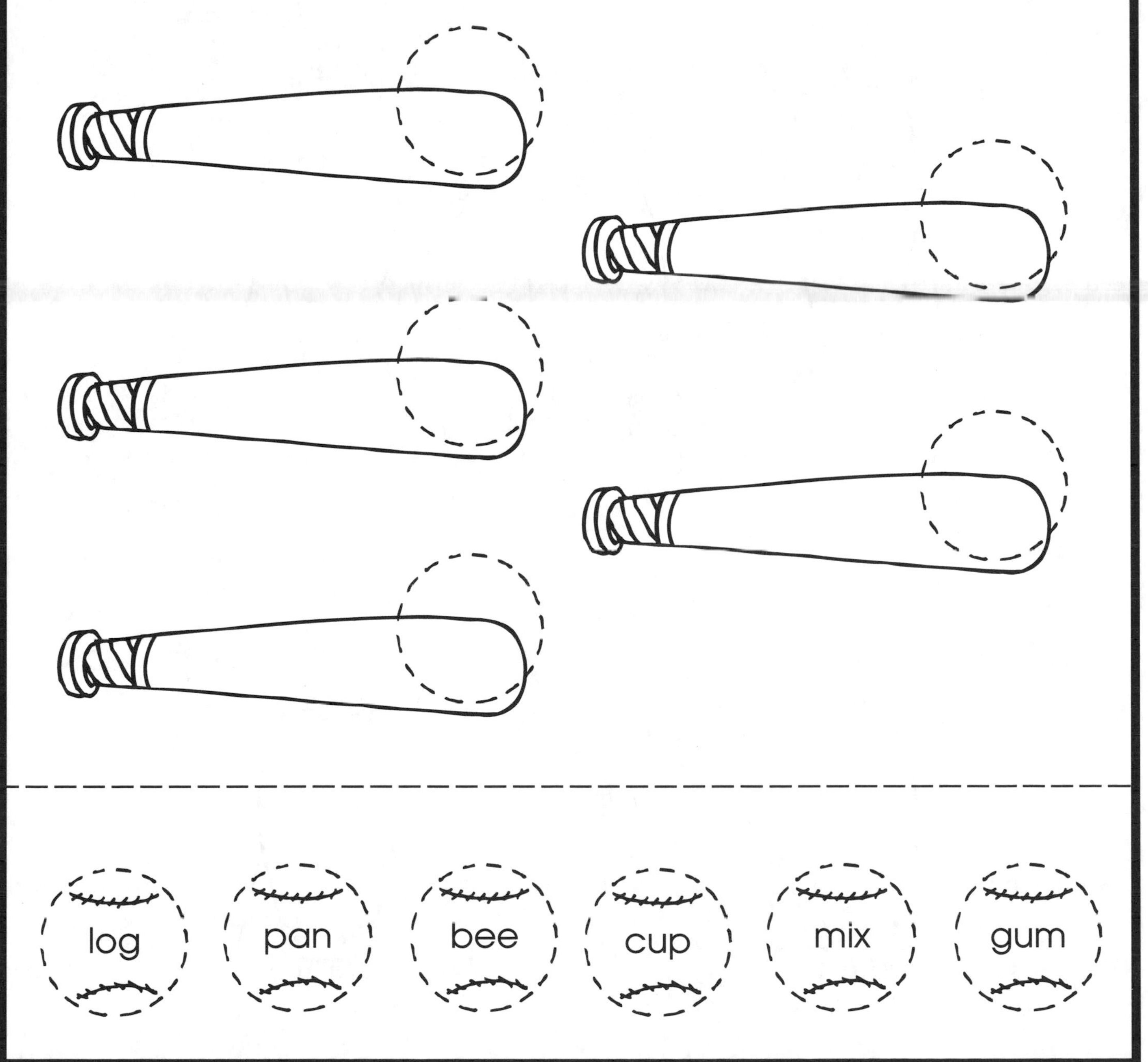

Blast Off!

The words below end with **two consonants** after **one vowel**. The vowel is short. Read the words.

vcc	v c c	v c c	v cc
blast	**lend**	**jump**	**moss**

Color the rockets with the short vowel pattern. Read the words.

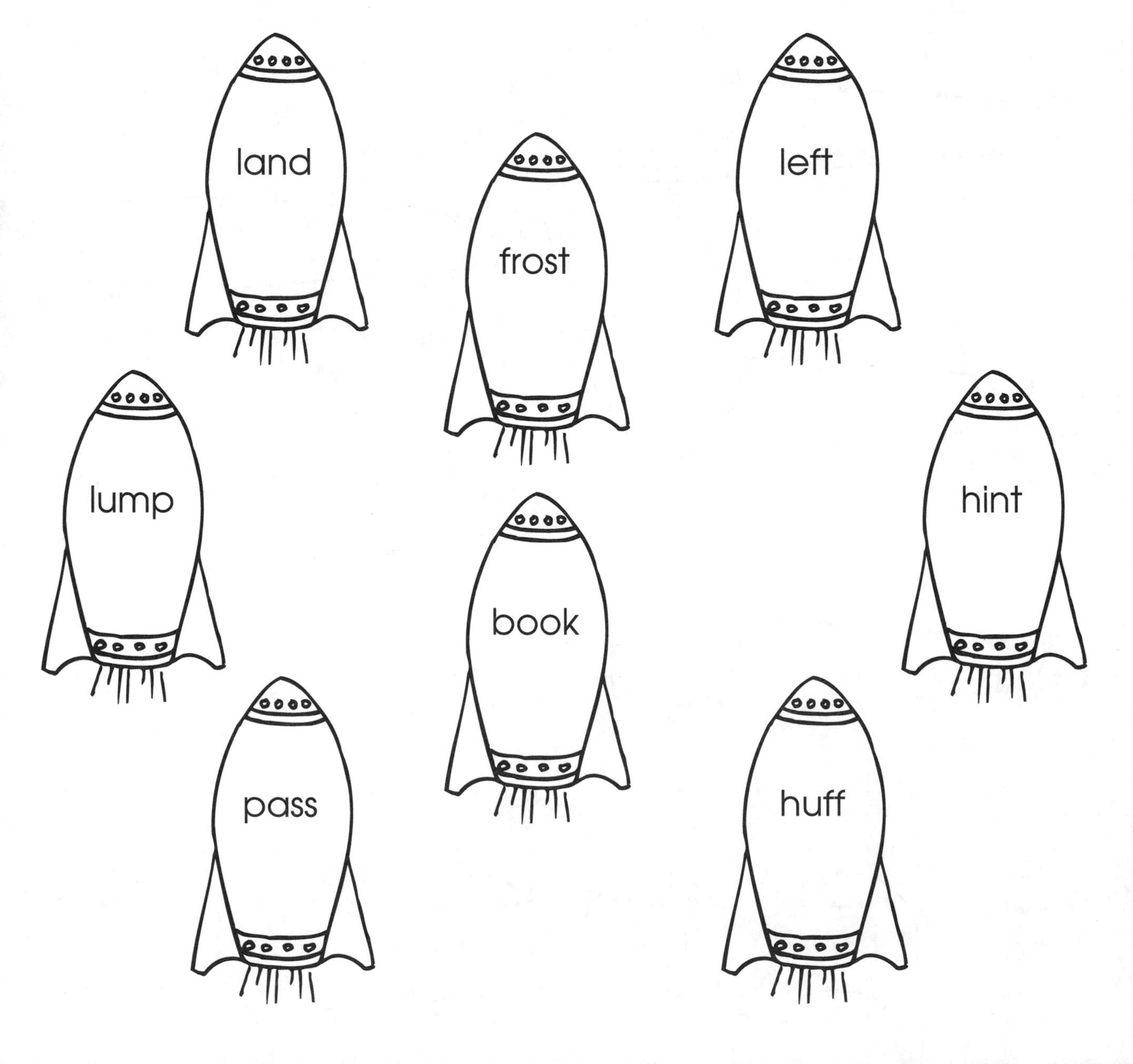

Fish!

The words below end with **two consonants** after **one vowel**. The vowel is short. The **sh**, **th**, **ck**, each have their own sounds. Read the words.

vcc	v c c	vcc
fish	**deck**	**bath**

Circle the fish with the short vowel pattern. Read the words.

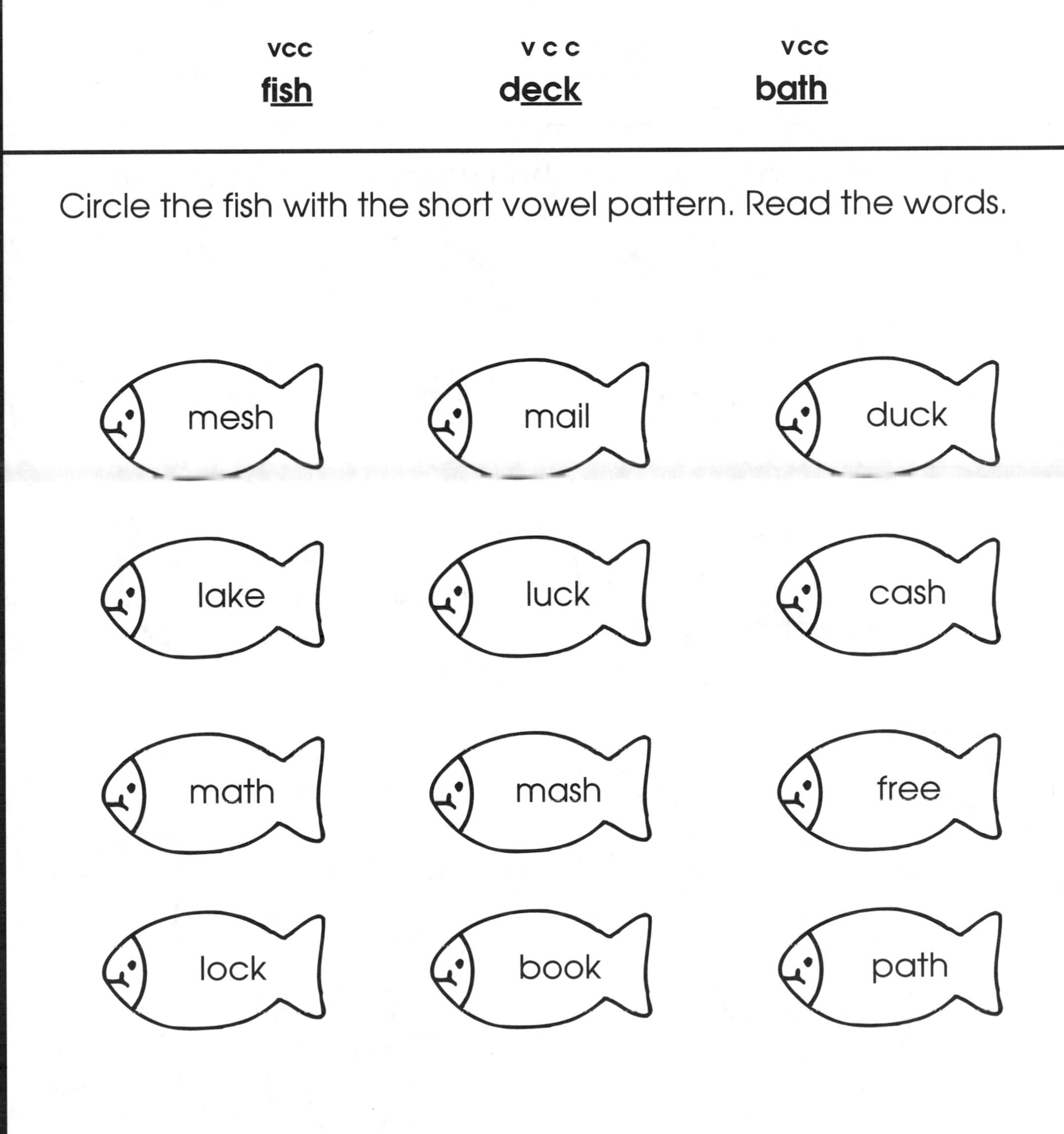

Dunk It!

The words below end with **two consonants** after **one vowel**. The vowel is short. The nk, and ng each have their own sounds. Read the words.

vc c	v c c	vc c	v c c
ring	**rang**	**sink**	**sank**

Color the basketballs with the short vowel pattern. Read the words.

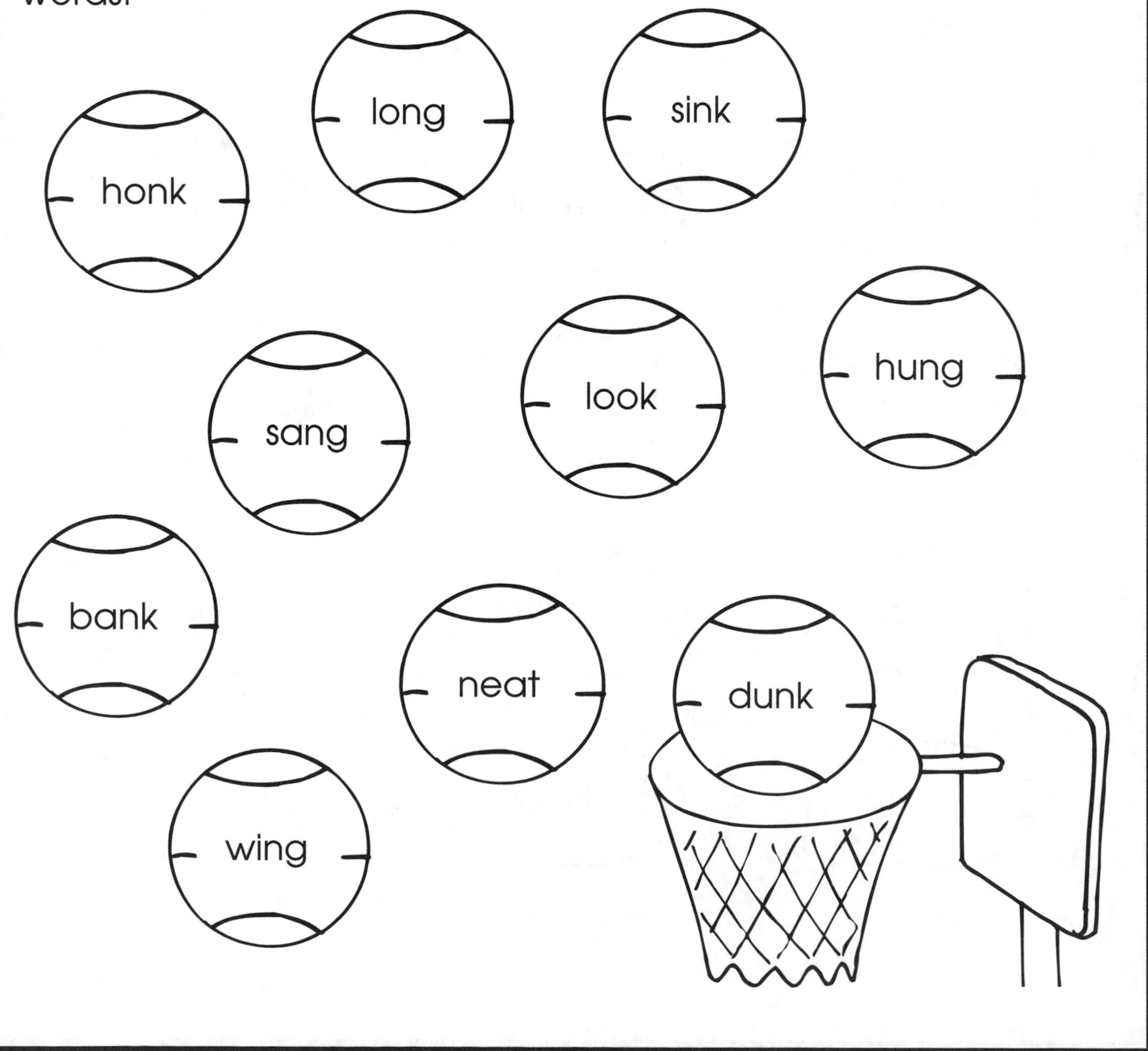

Catch!

The words below end with **three consonants** at the end after **one vowel**. The vowels are short. The **tch** and **ch** have their own sounds.

vccc	vcc c	vccc
catch	**lunch**	**bench**

Cut out the baseballs with the short vowel pattern. Paste them on the baseball mitts. Read the words.

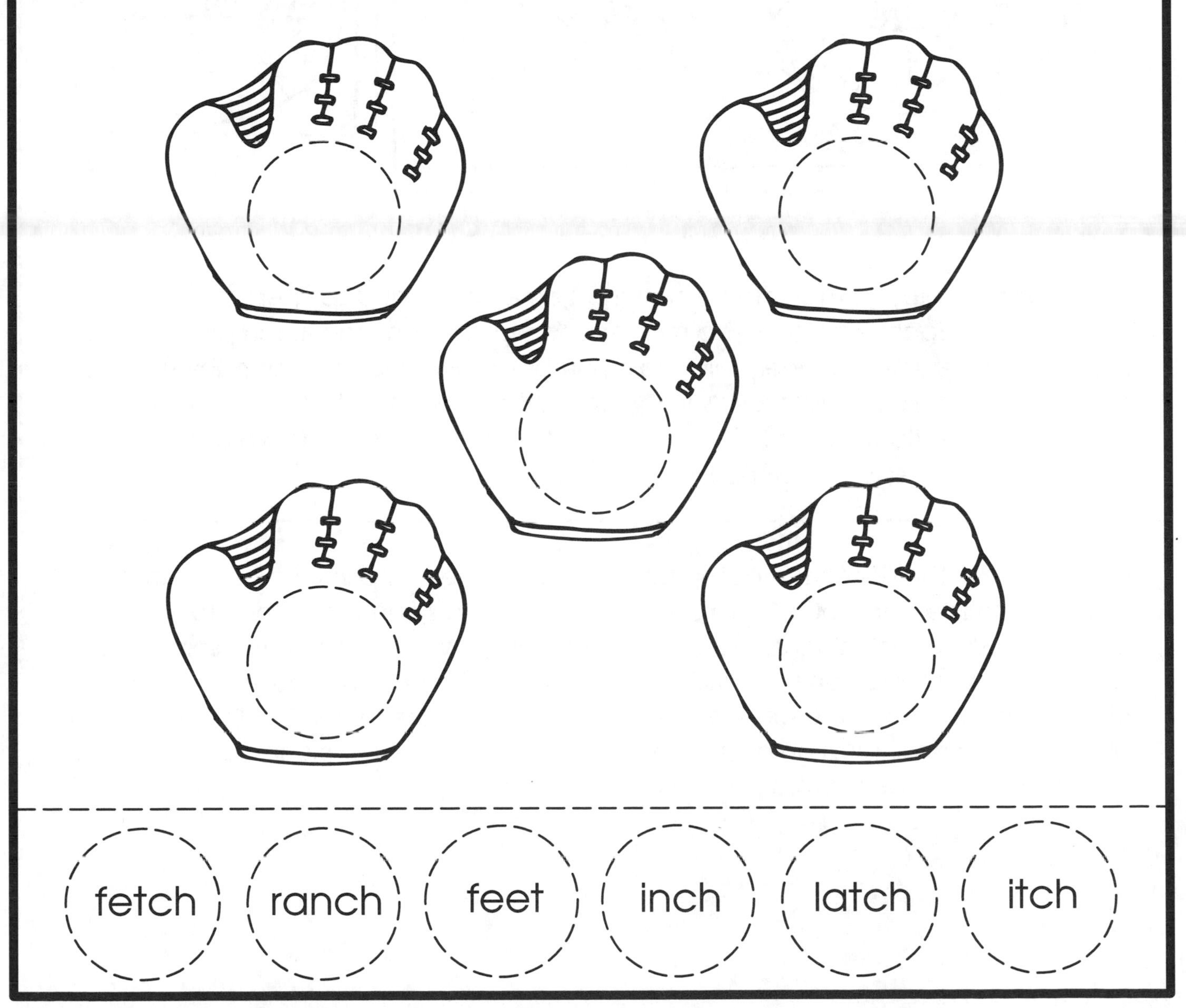

Short Vowel Run

Short Vowel Run

(Short Vowel Pattern)

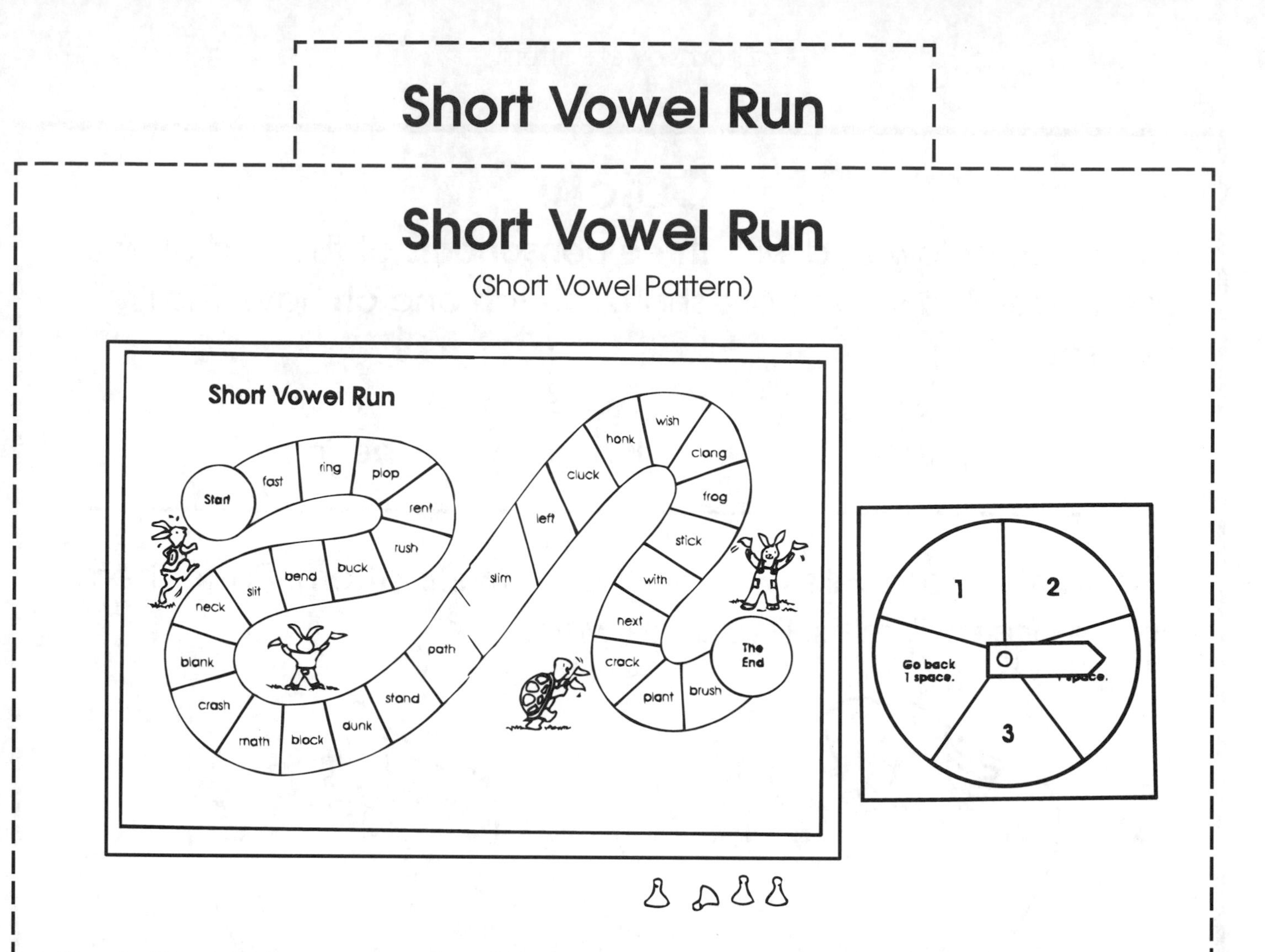

How to Play: 4 players may play. Place the game board and spinner wheel in playing area. Each player takes a marker and places it on Start. Each player in turn spins the wheel. If the spinner points to a number, player moves that many spaces on the game board. Player reads the word on the space landed. If the spinner points to a direction, player follows that direction. Player reads the word on the space landed. The winner is the first player to reach The End.

How to Make: Duplicate the game board pages, wheel and spinner. Glue game board on to the inside of a file folder. Glue wheel and spinner onto oak tag and cut out. Punch a hole in spinner and in the middle of the wheel. Fasten the spinner to wheel with a brass fastener. Provide 4 markers. Store spinner wheel and markers in a clasp envelope. Glue the envelope to the back of the file folder. Duplicate playing directions, game illustration and game tab and cut. Glue directions and illustration onto the front of the file folder. Glue game tab on file tab.

Short Vowel Run

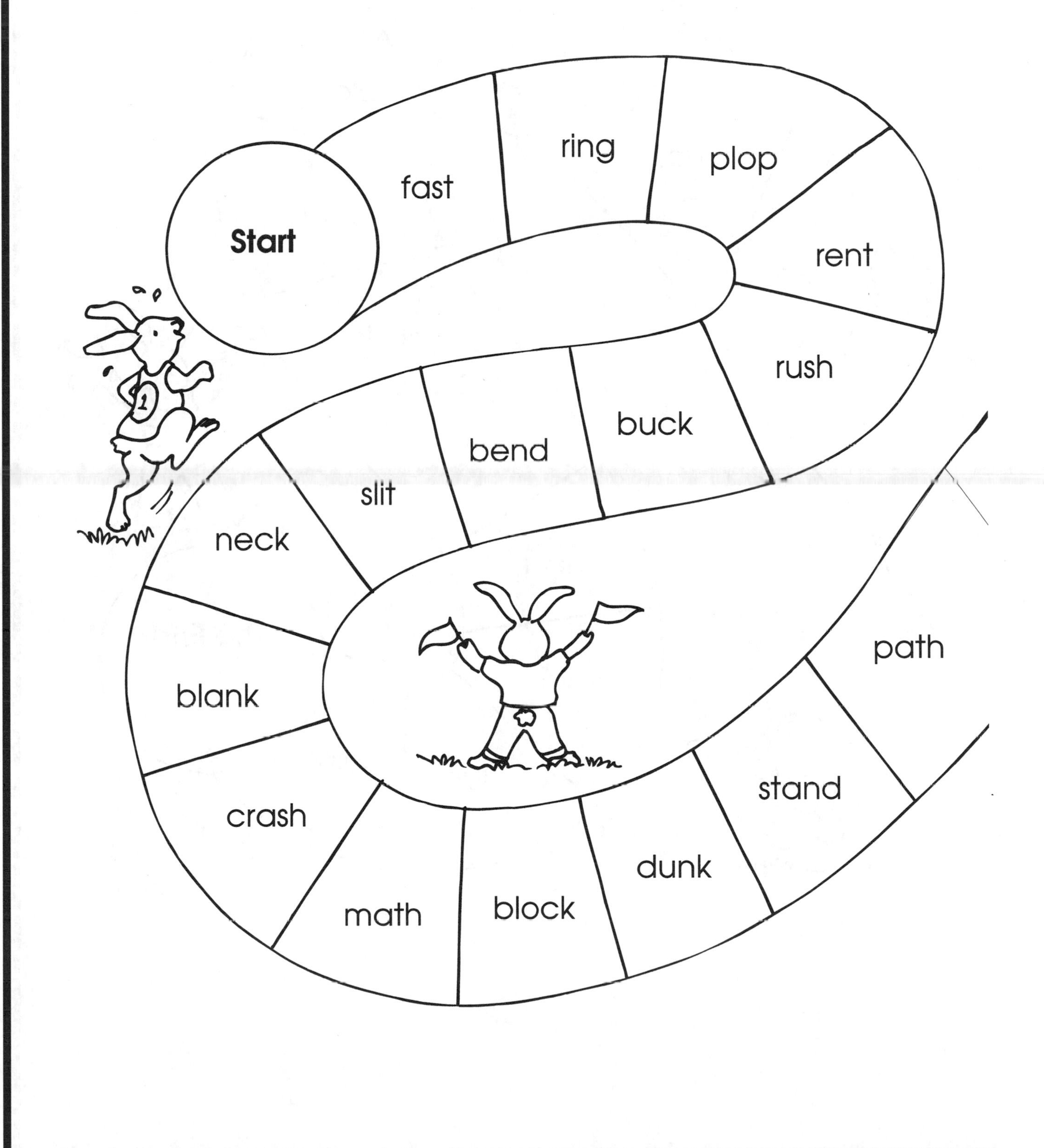

Short Vowel Run

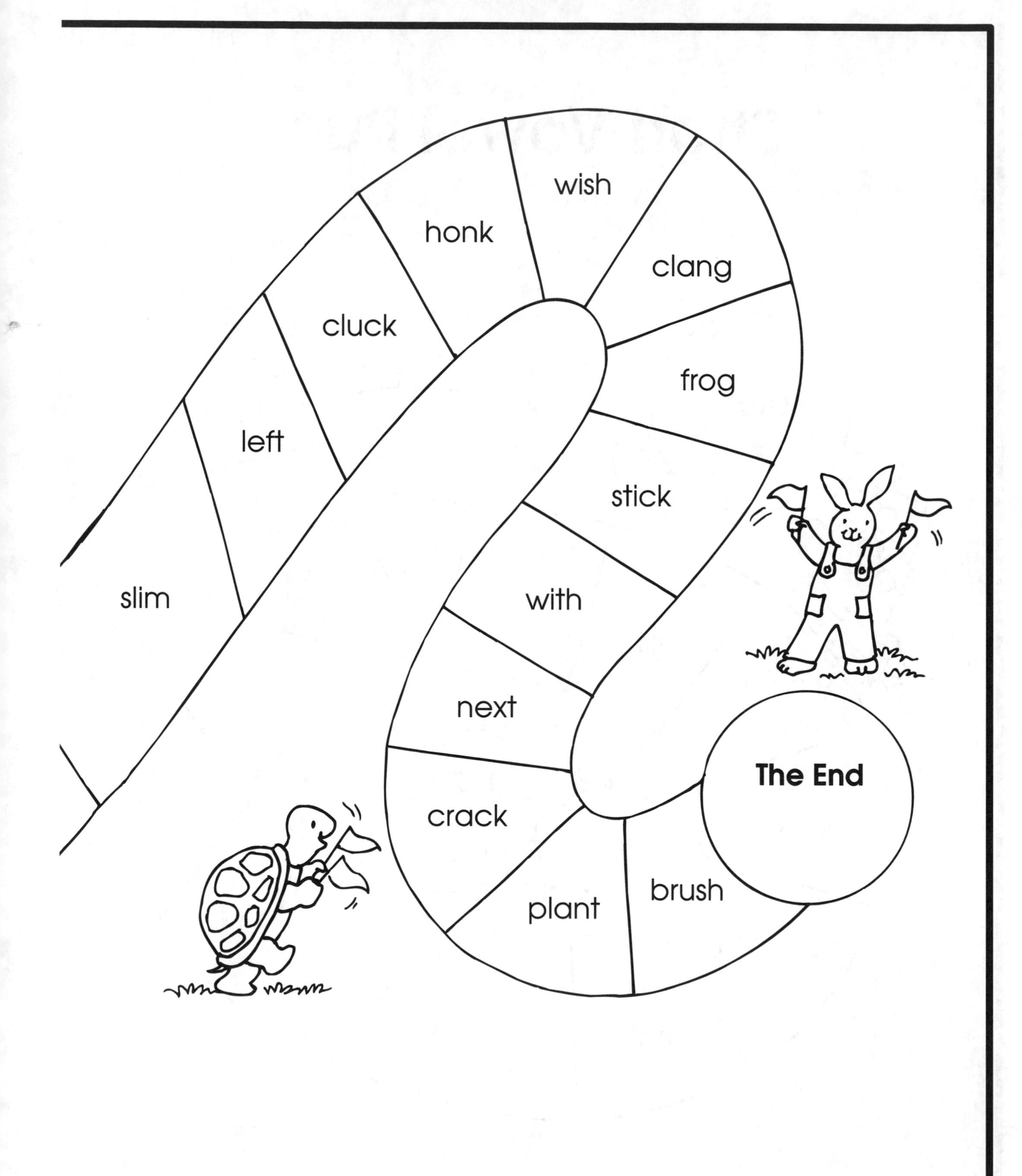

Short Vowel Run

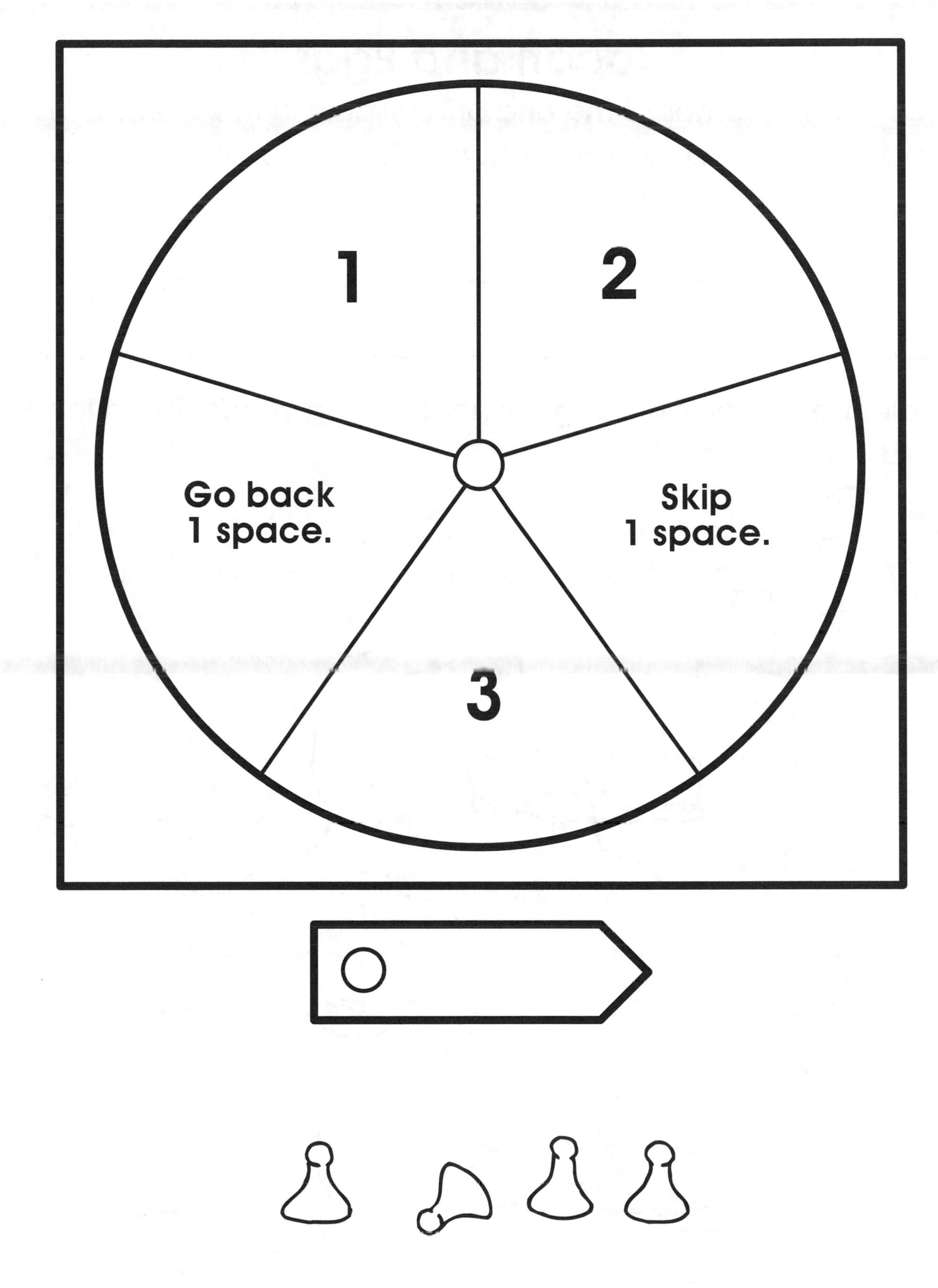

Attach spinner to wheel with a brass fastener. Provide 4 markers.

Bacon and Eggs

The vowel **a** comes **at the end** of a syllable in the words below. The vowel is **long** and says its name. Read the long **a** words. The words are divided into syllables.

v	v	v
ba/con	**la/dy**	**a/pron**

Circle the bacon and eggs with the long **a** words. Read the words.

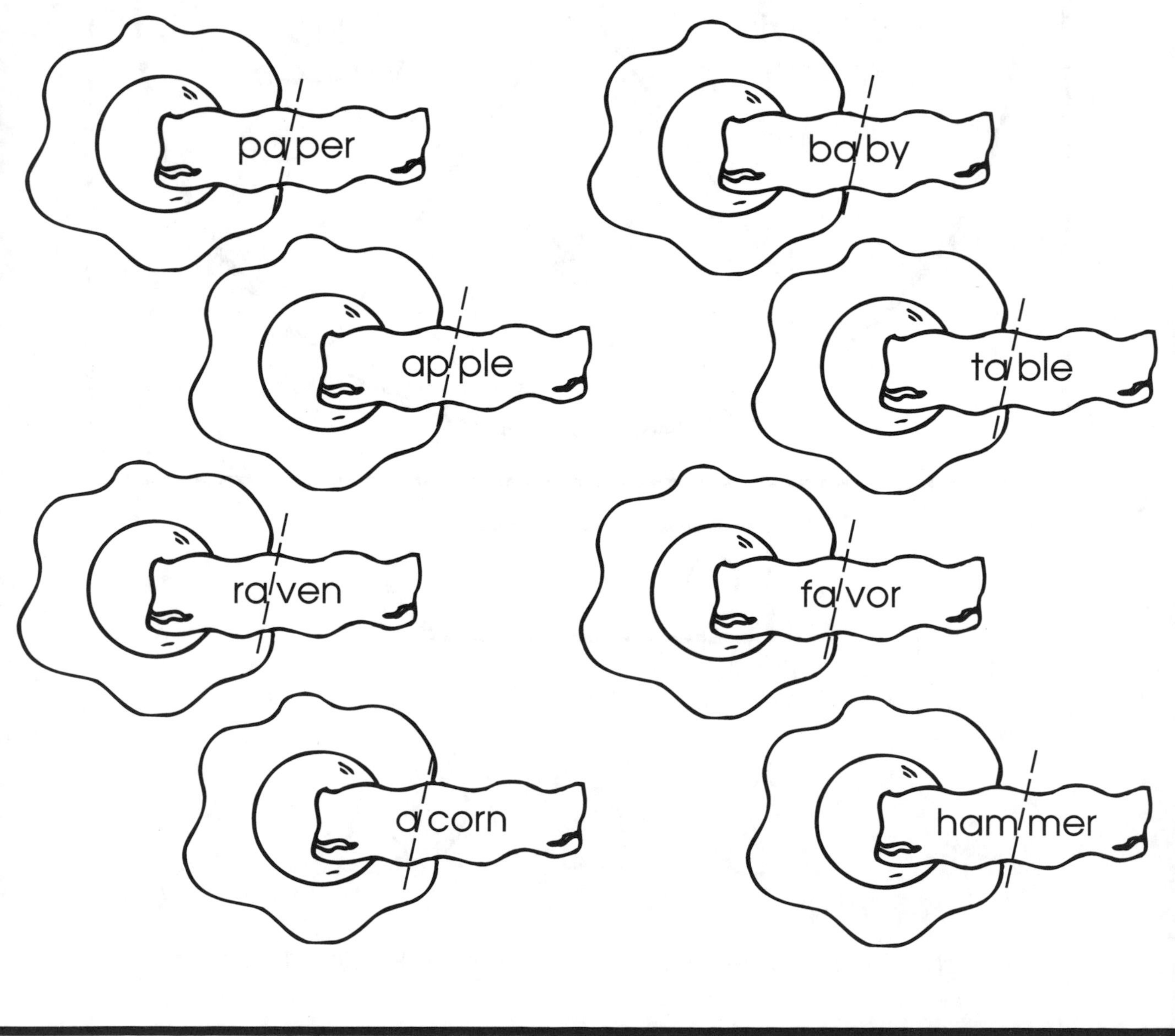

Relay It!

The vowel **e** comes **at the end** of a syllable in the words below. The vowel is long and says its name. Read the long **e** words. The words are divided into syllables.

me **Pe/ter** **re/lay**

Color the circles with the long **e** words. Read the words.

Spider Web

The vowel <u>i</u> comes **at the end** of a syllable in the words below. The vowel is **long** and says its name. Read the long <u>i</u> words. The words are divided into syllables.

<u>spi</u>/der **<u>Hi</u>!** **<u>ti</u>/ger**

Cut and paste the circles with the long <u>i</u> words.
Read the words.

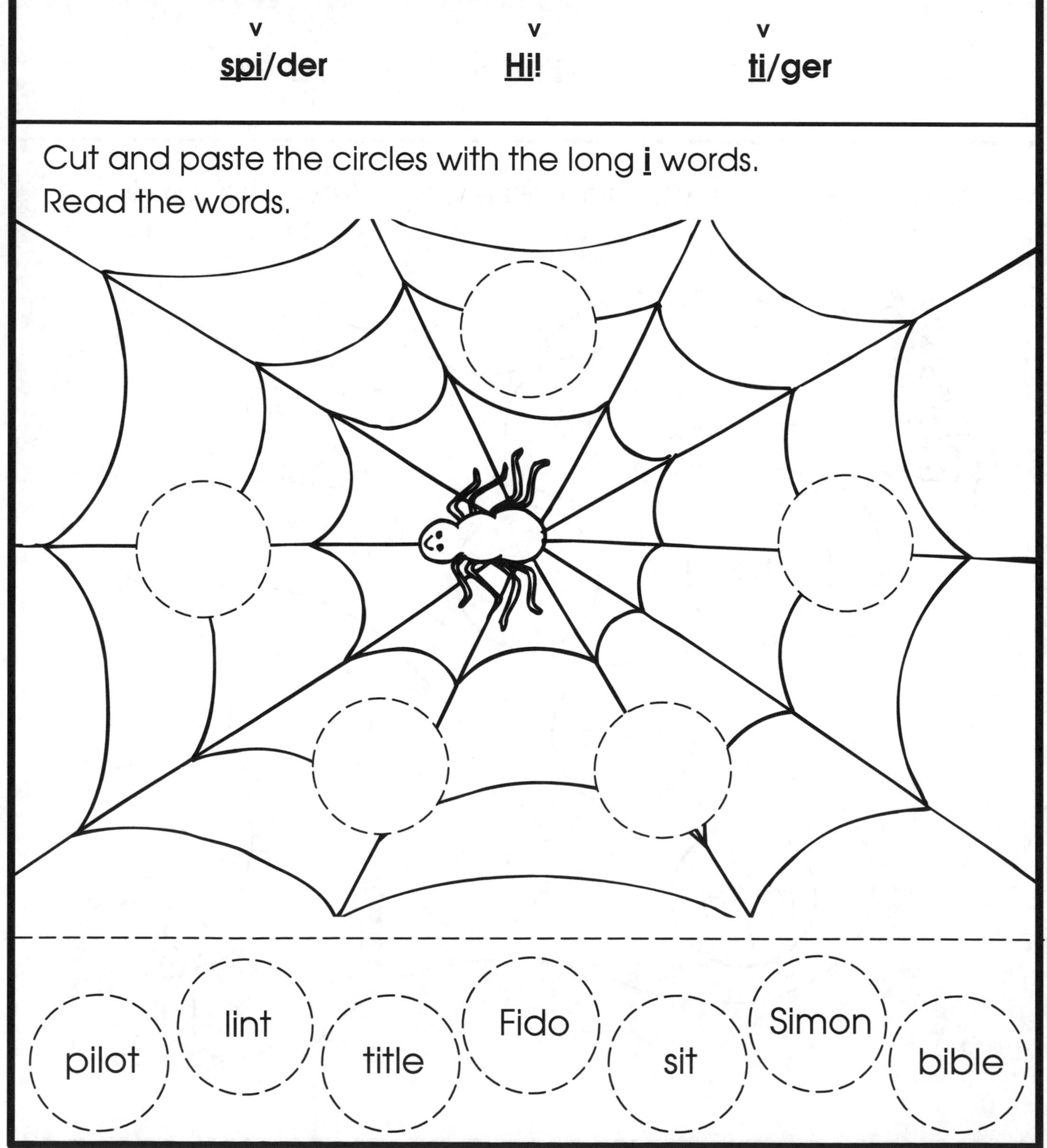

Robot

The vowel <u>**o**</u> comes **at the end** of a syllable in the words below. The vowel is **long** and says its name. Read the long **o** words. The words are divided into syllables.

v	v	v v
<u>ro</u>/bot	**<u>no</u>**	**<u>po</u>/<u>lo</u>**

Color the parts on the robot with the long <u>o</u> words.
Read the words.

Music Notes

The vowel **u** comes **at the end** of a syllable in the words below. The vowel is **long** and says its name. Read the long **u** words. The words are divided into syllables.

Color the music notes with the long **u** words. Read the words.

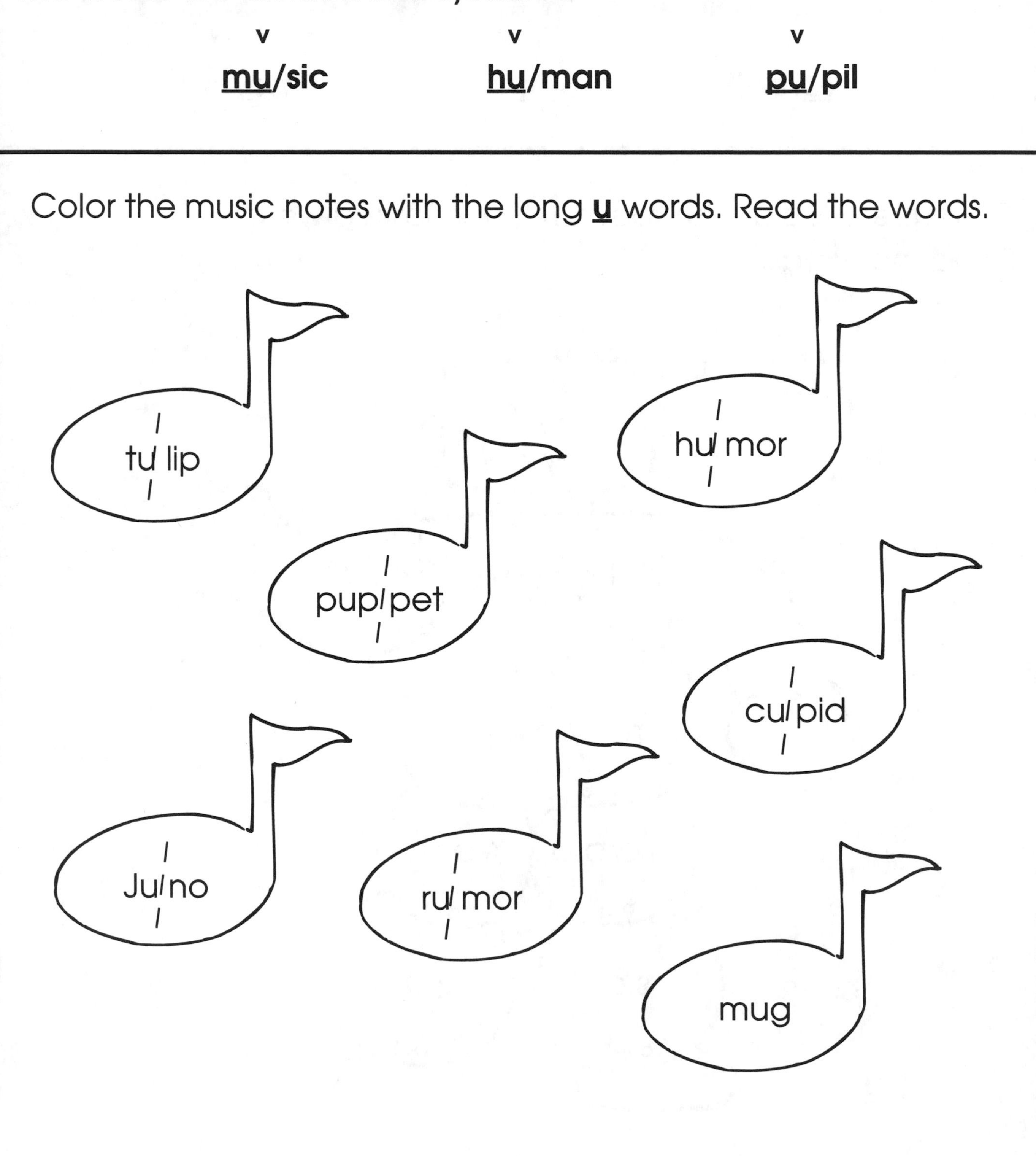

Long Vowel Train

Long Vowel Train

(Open Syllable)

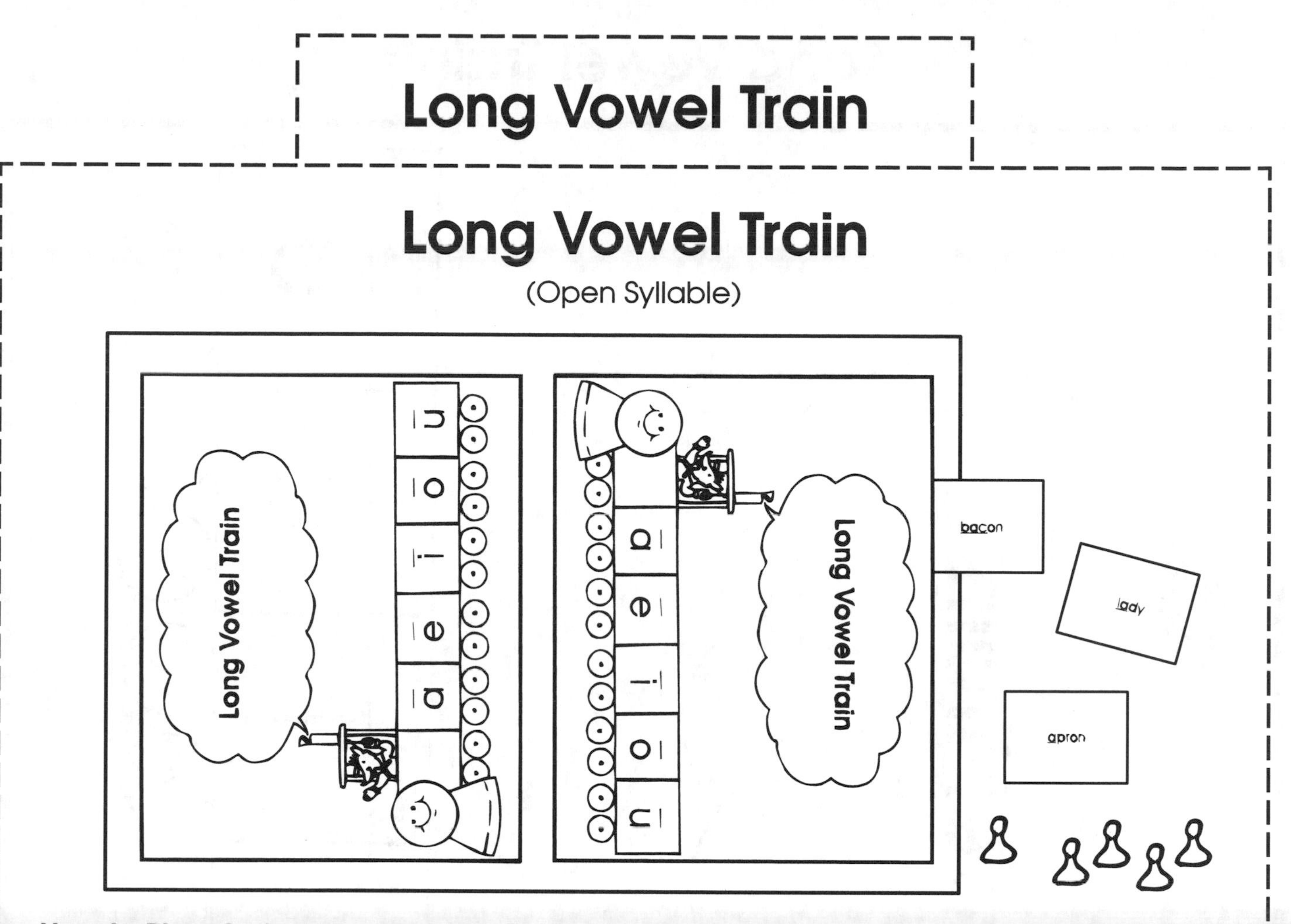

How to Play: 2 players may play. Set the game board in playing area. Shuffle and place the word cards face down in a pile. Each player takes five markers and chooses a train to play. Each player in turn takes a card and reads the word on it. Players check the underlined part of the word for long vowel sound. Players place a marker on the car on the train that has that vowel. If a player picks a card for a long vowel car that already has a marker on it, he misses his turn. He/she must still read the word on the card. The card is discarded. The player who fills all of his cars with markers first is the winner.

How to Make: Duplicate the game board two times. Glue on the inside of a file folder. Duplicate the long vowel word cards. Glue onto oak tag and cut out the cards. Provide five markers for each player (buttons, game markers, beans, etc.). Store word cards and markers in a clasp envelope. Glue envelope onto the back of the file folder. Duplicate the game directions, game illustration and game tab and cut. Glue directions and illustration to the front of the file folder. Glue game tab onto the file tab.

Long Vowel Train

Duplicate two times.

Long Vowel Train

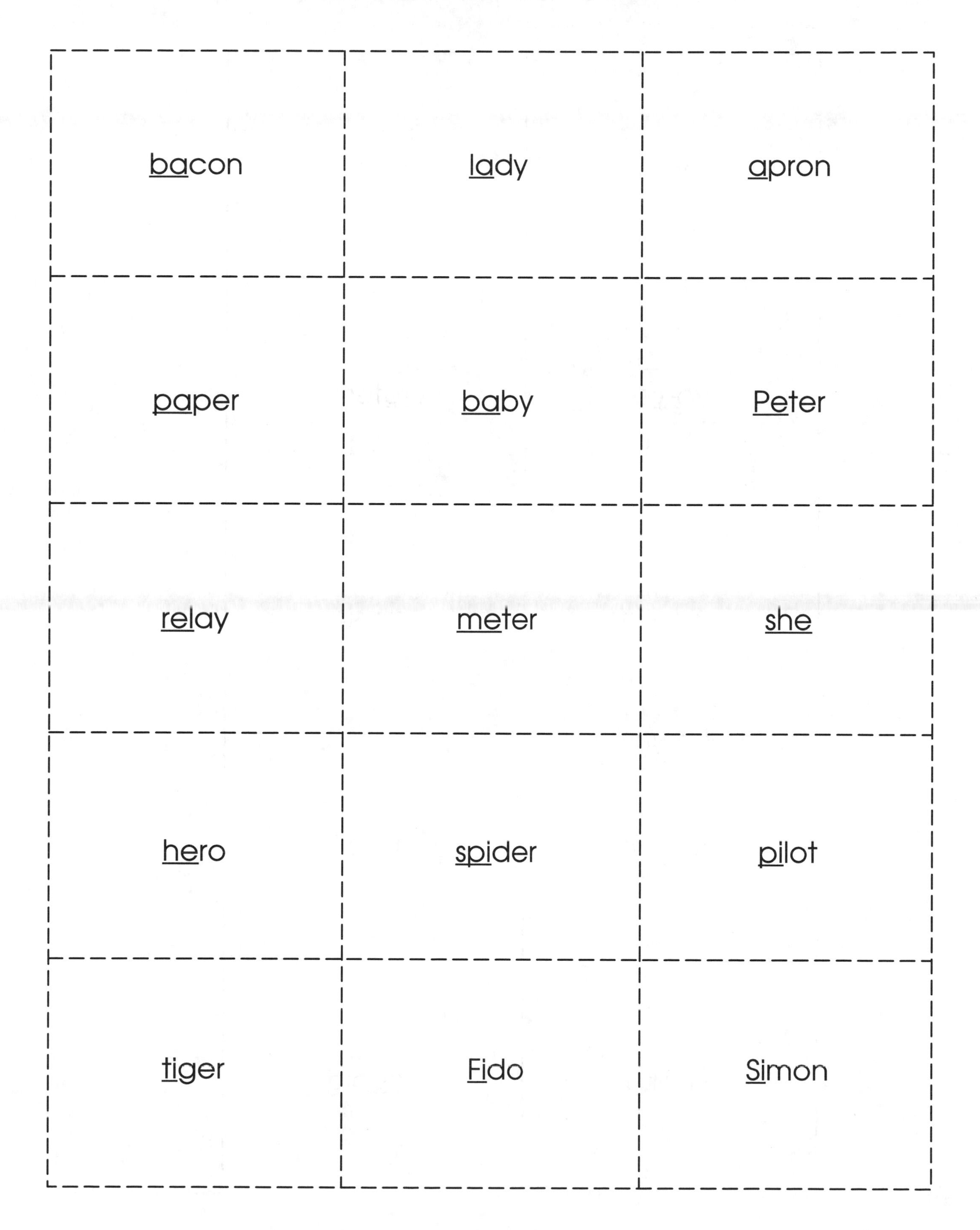

Long Vowel Train

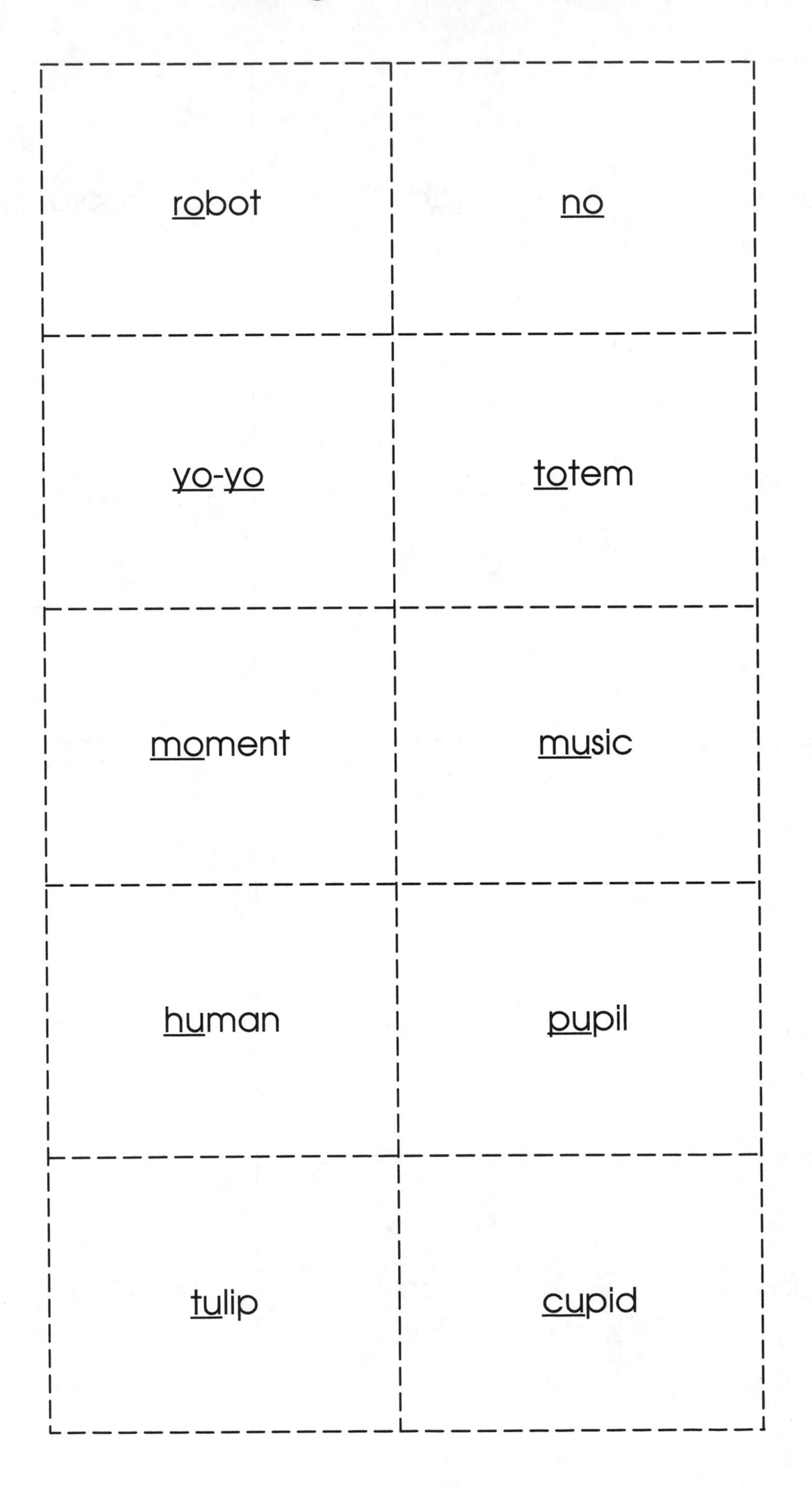

Bake a Cake

The word **cake** ends with a **vowel**, a **consonant**, and a **final e**. The **final e** is silent and makes the first vowel **a** long and say its name. Read the words below with the long **a** sound as in **cake**.

vc e	v c e	vc e
bake	**tape**	**cave**

Color the cakes with the long **a** words as in **cake**. Read the words.

cape

drape

game

plane

mat

gate

maze

fad

wave

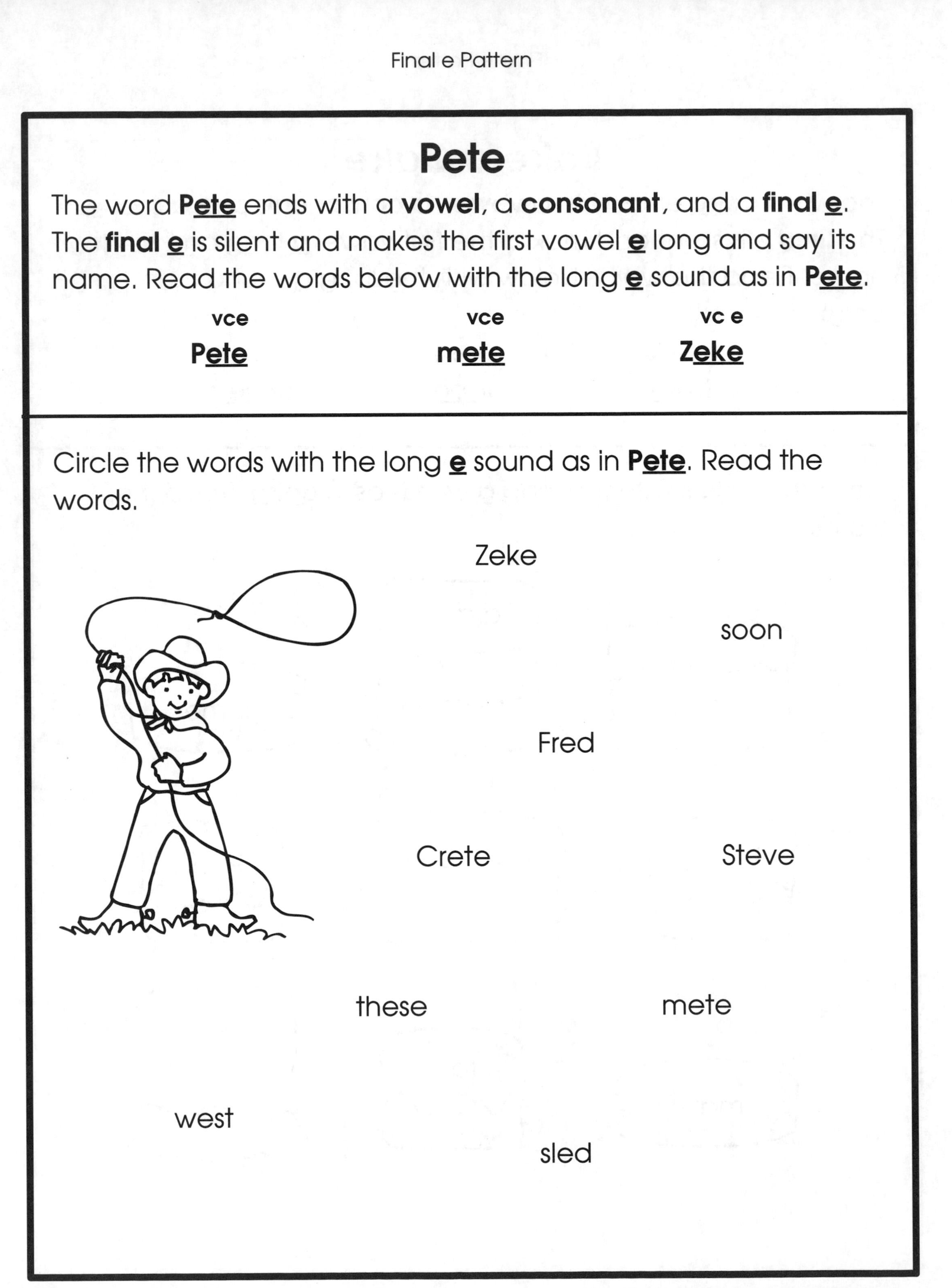

Pete

The word **Pete** ends with a **vowel**, a **consonant**, and a **final e**. The **final e** is silent and makes the first vowel **e** long and say its name. Read the words below with the long **e** sound as in **Pete**.

vce	vce	vc e
Pete	**mete**	**Zeke**

Circle the words with the long **e** sound as in **Pete**. Read the words.

Zeke

soon

Fred

Crete

Steve

these

mete

west

sled

Dive

The word **d<u>ive</u>** ends with a **vowel**, a **consonant**, and a **final <u>e</u>**. The **final <u>e</u>** is silent and makes the first vowel <u>i</u> long and say its name. Read the words below with the long <u>i</u> sound as in **d<u>ive</u>**.

vce	vce	vce
hive	**tide**	**mine**

Cut and paste the shells with the long <u>i</u> words as in **d<u>ive</u>**. Read the words.

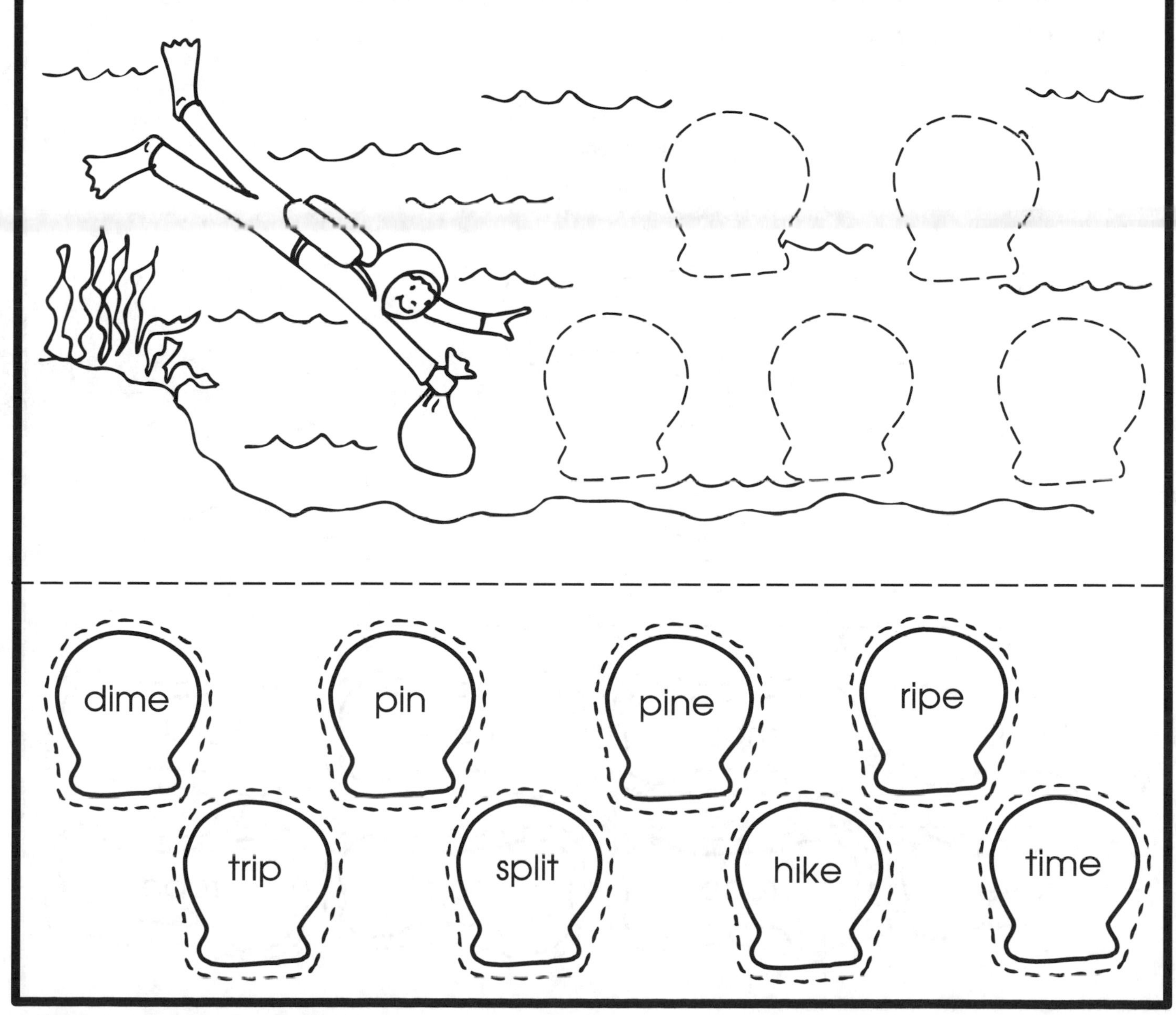

Bones

The word **bone** ends with a **vowel**, a **consonant**, and a **final e**. The **final e** is silent and makes the first vowel **o** long and say its name. Read the words below with the long **o** sound as in **bone**.

vc e	v c e	vce
cone	**rope**	**hole**

Cut and paste the bones with the long **o** words as in **bone**. Read the words.

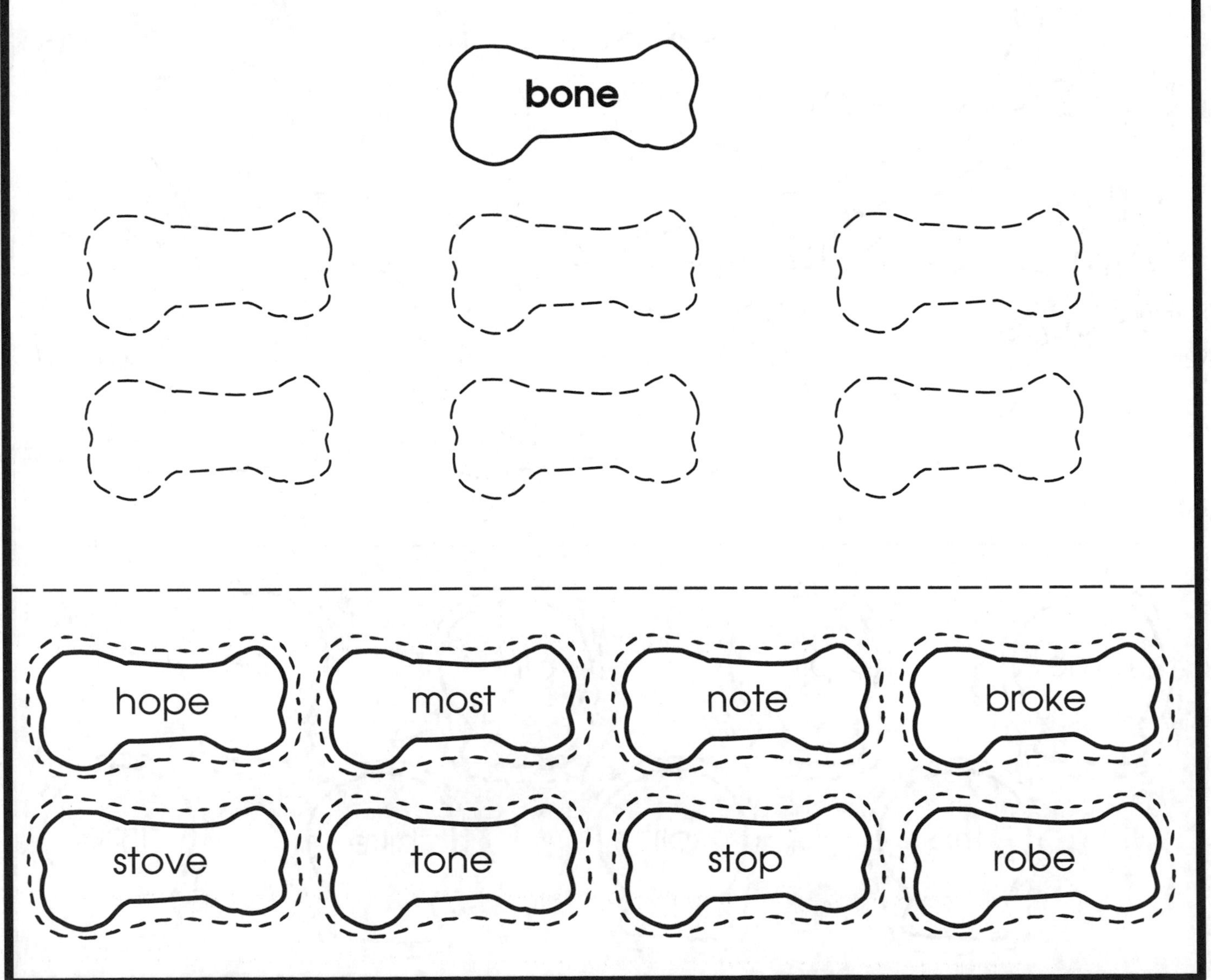

Cute Mule!

The word **mule** ends with a **vowel**, a **consonant**, and a **final e**. The **final e** is silent and makes the first vowel **u** long and say its name. Read the words below with the long **u** sound as in **mule**.

vce	vce	vce
cube	**dune**	**tube**

Color the bags with the long **u** words as in m**ule**. Read the words.

mule

tune	huge	brush
June	cut	cube
fun	mule	cute

Final e BINGO

Final e BINGO

(Final e Pattern)

How to Play: 2 players may play. Shuffle the word cards and place face down in playing area. Each player takes a BINGO playing card. Each player in turn takes a word card and reads the final e word on it. Players place the cards in the column for their final e sound on their playing card. If a player has no more spaces for a final e word, he/she misses his/her turn. Card is placed back in playing area face down. The player who makes a BINGO first is the winner. Players may also play for block out by continuing to play. First player to fill every playing space with word cards is the Super Winner!

How to Make: Duplicate the Final e BINGO playing card two times. Glue onto oak tag. Duplicate the word cards two times. Glue onto oak tag and cut out the cards. Store word cards and game boards in a clasp envelope. Duplicate the game directions. Glue on the front of the envelope.

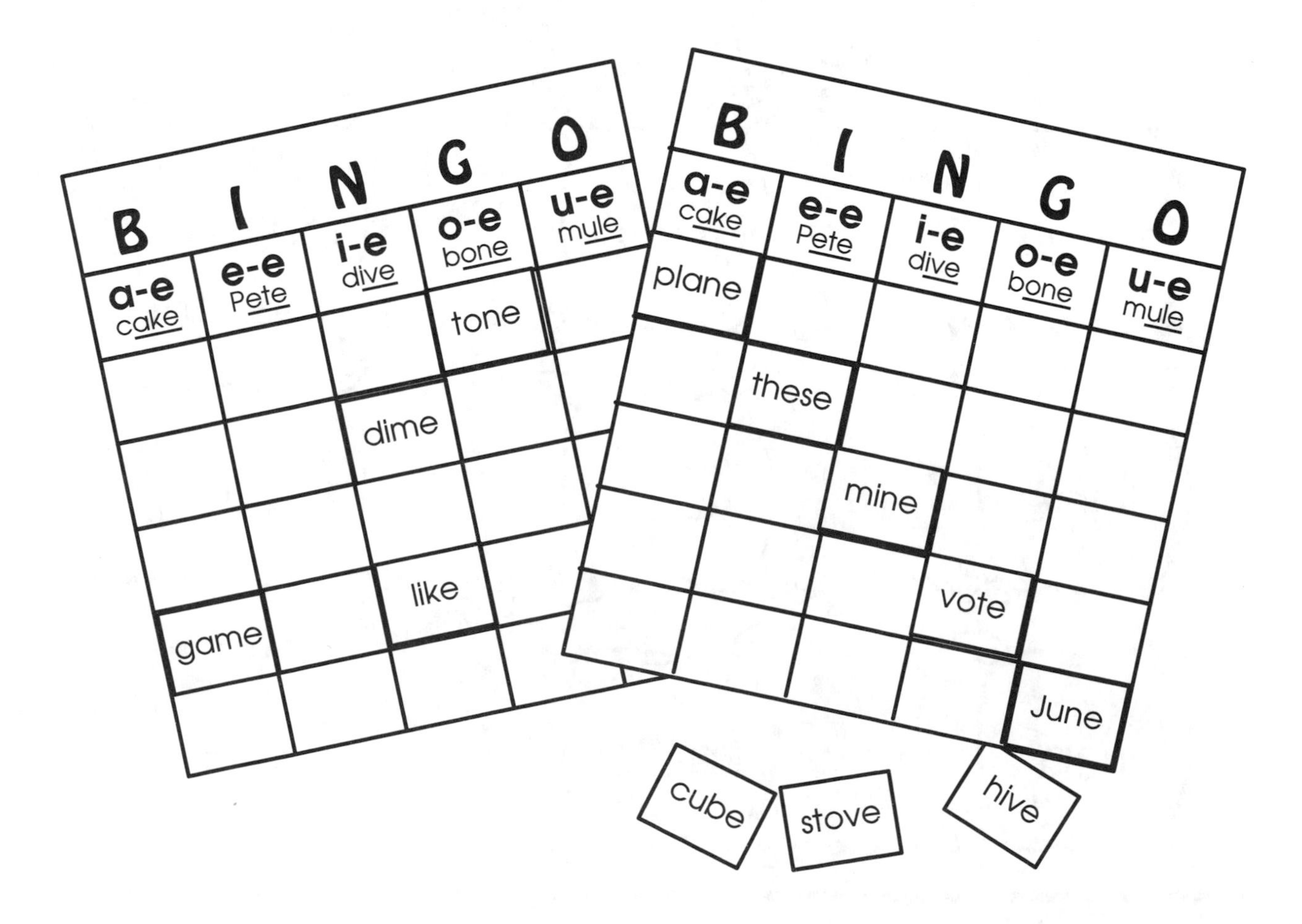

Final e BINGO

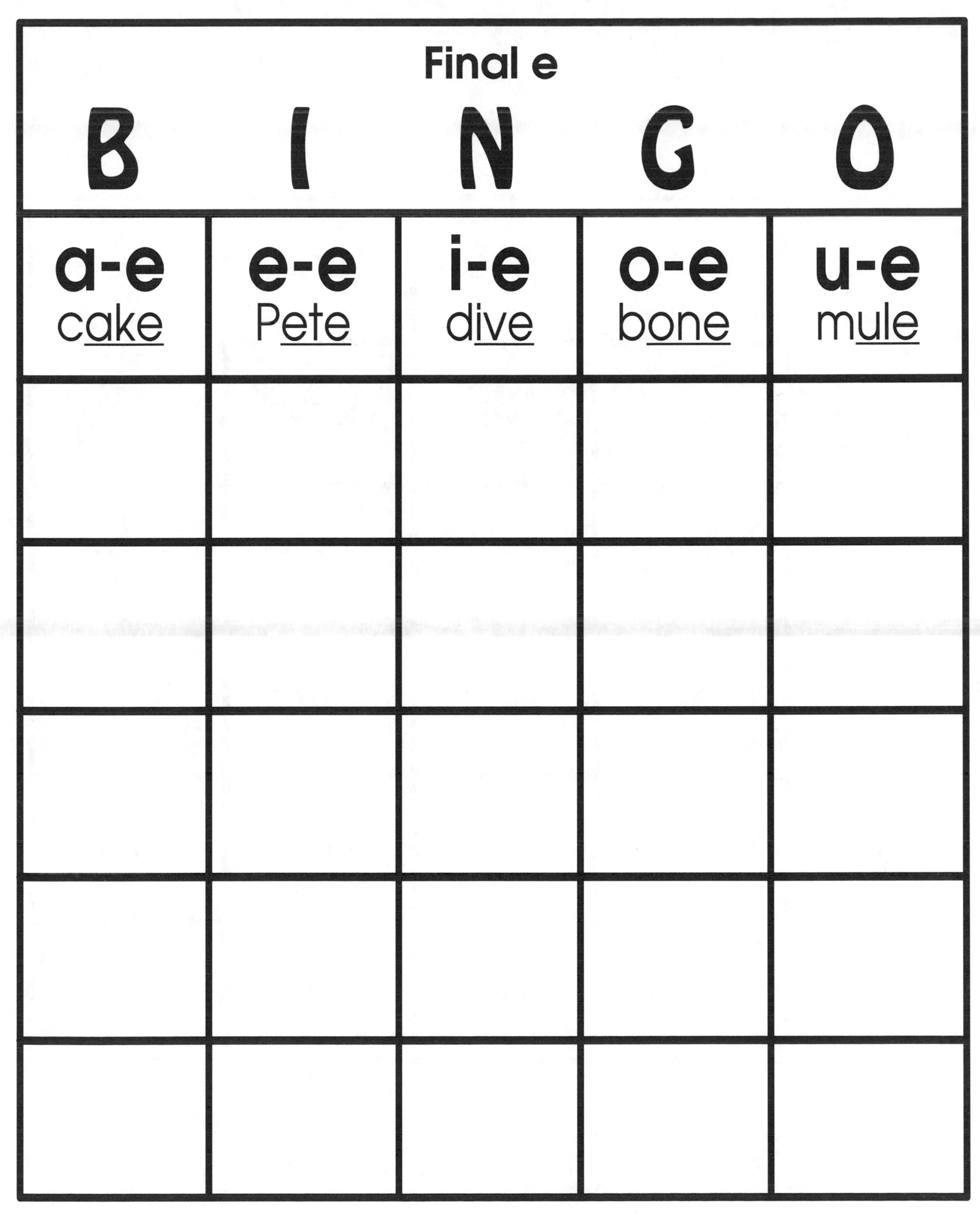

Final e B	I	N	G	O
a-e cake	e-e Pete	i-e dive	o-e bone	u-e mule

Duplicate two times.

Final e BINGO

tame	mete	hive	tone	cube
lake	Zeke	five	cone	tune
save	these	dime	rope	cute
plane	Steve	mine	stove	dune
wade	Crete	like	zone	June
game	Pete	ripe	vote	fume

Duplicate two times.

Stars

In **ar** as in **star**, and **or** as in **corn**, the **r** is bossy. The **r** controls the vowel sounds. Read the words below with **ar** and **or**.

ar	or
car far	fort horn

Color the stars with **ar** words yellow. Color the stars with **or** words blue. Read the words.

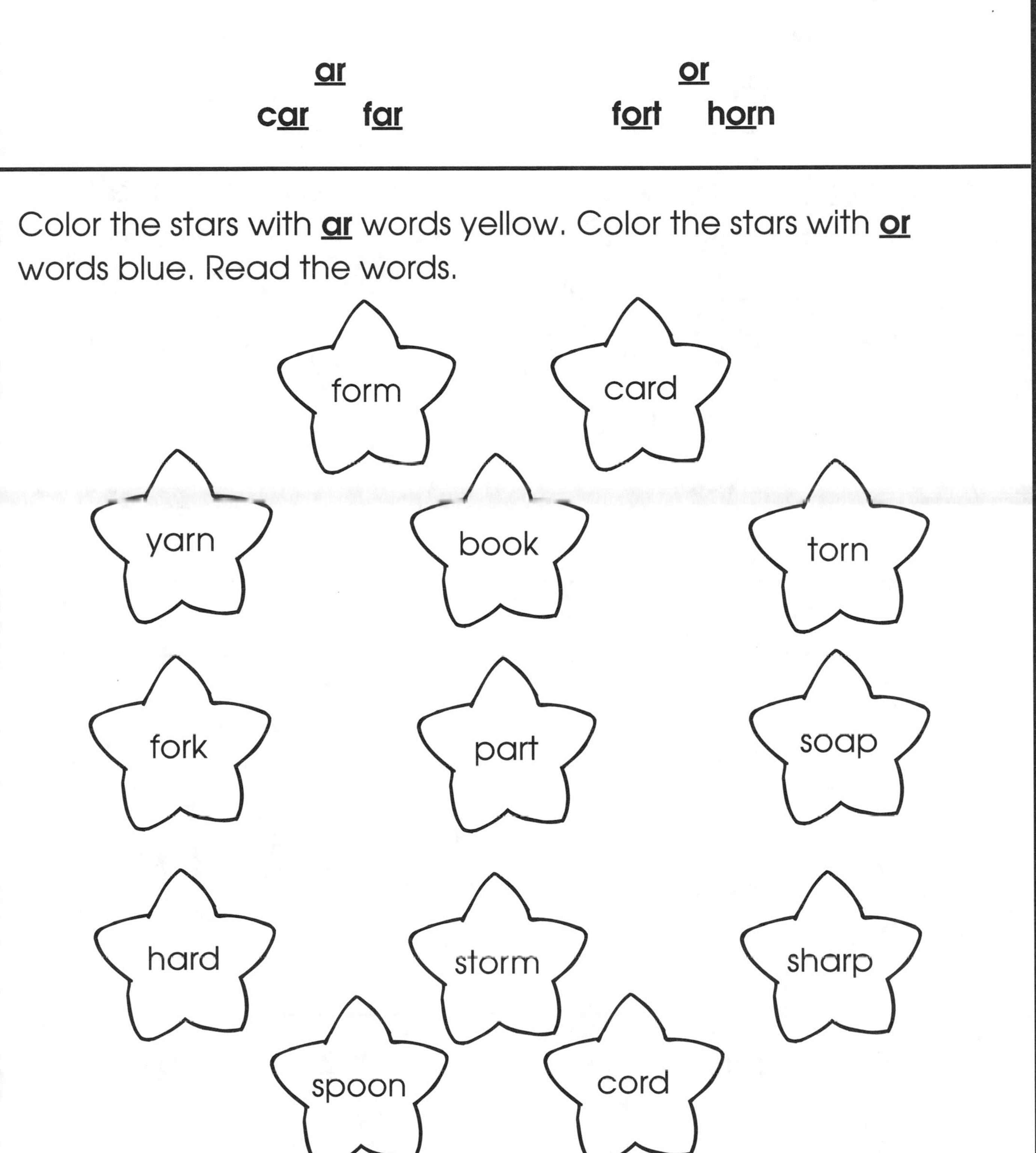

Surf Boards

In **er**, **ir**, and **ur**, the **r** is bossy. The **r** controls the vowel sounds. Read the words below with **er**, **ir**, and **ur**.

er	ir	ur
fern perk	sir dirt	turn surf

Write the **er**, **ir**, and **ur** words on their surf boards. Read the words.

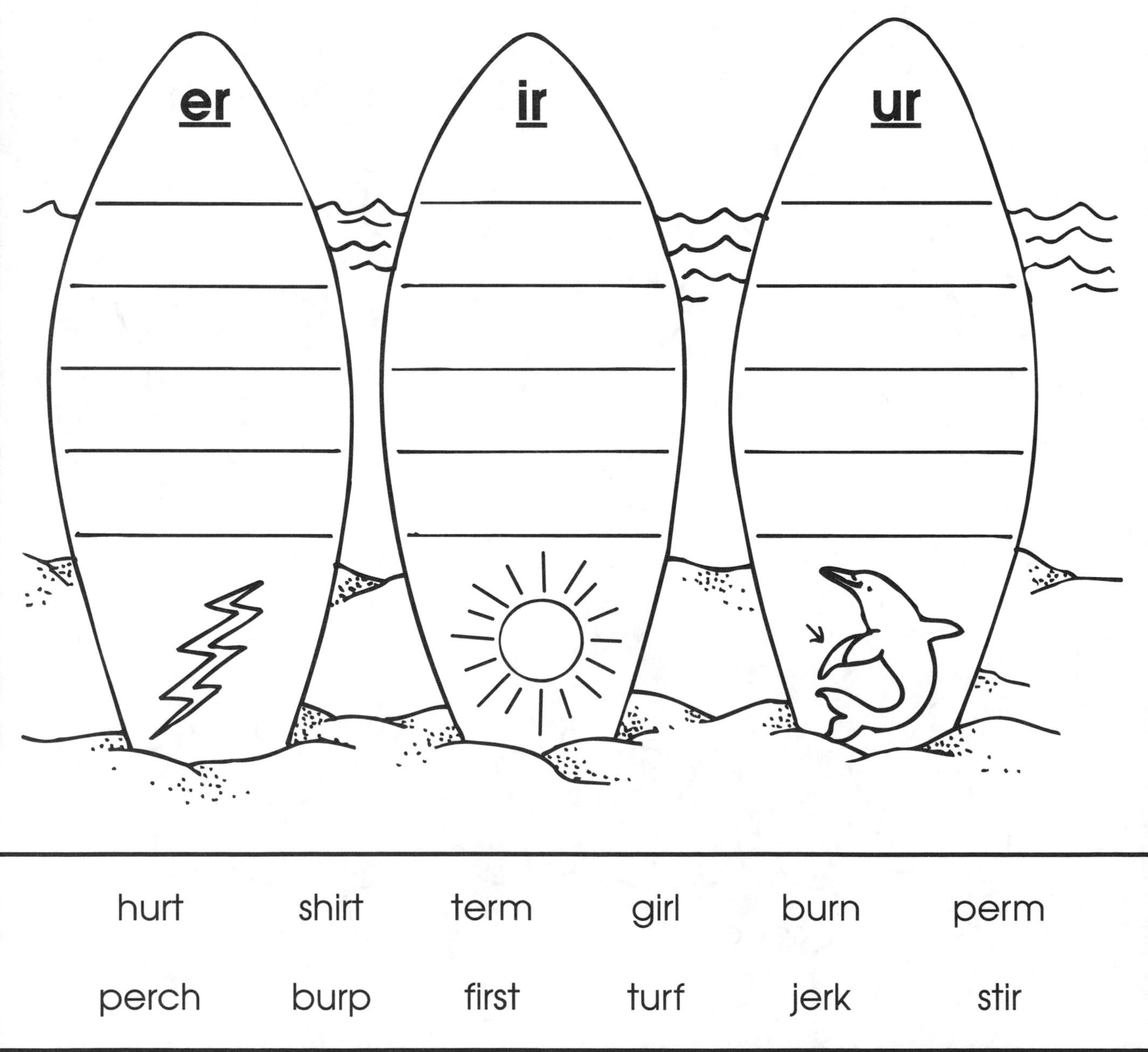

hurt	shirt	term	girl	burn	perm
perch	burp	first	turf	jerk	stir

Bossy R

Bossy R

(R Controlled Pattern)

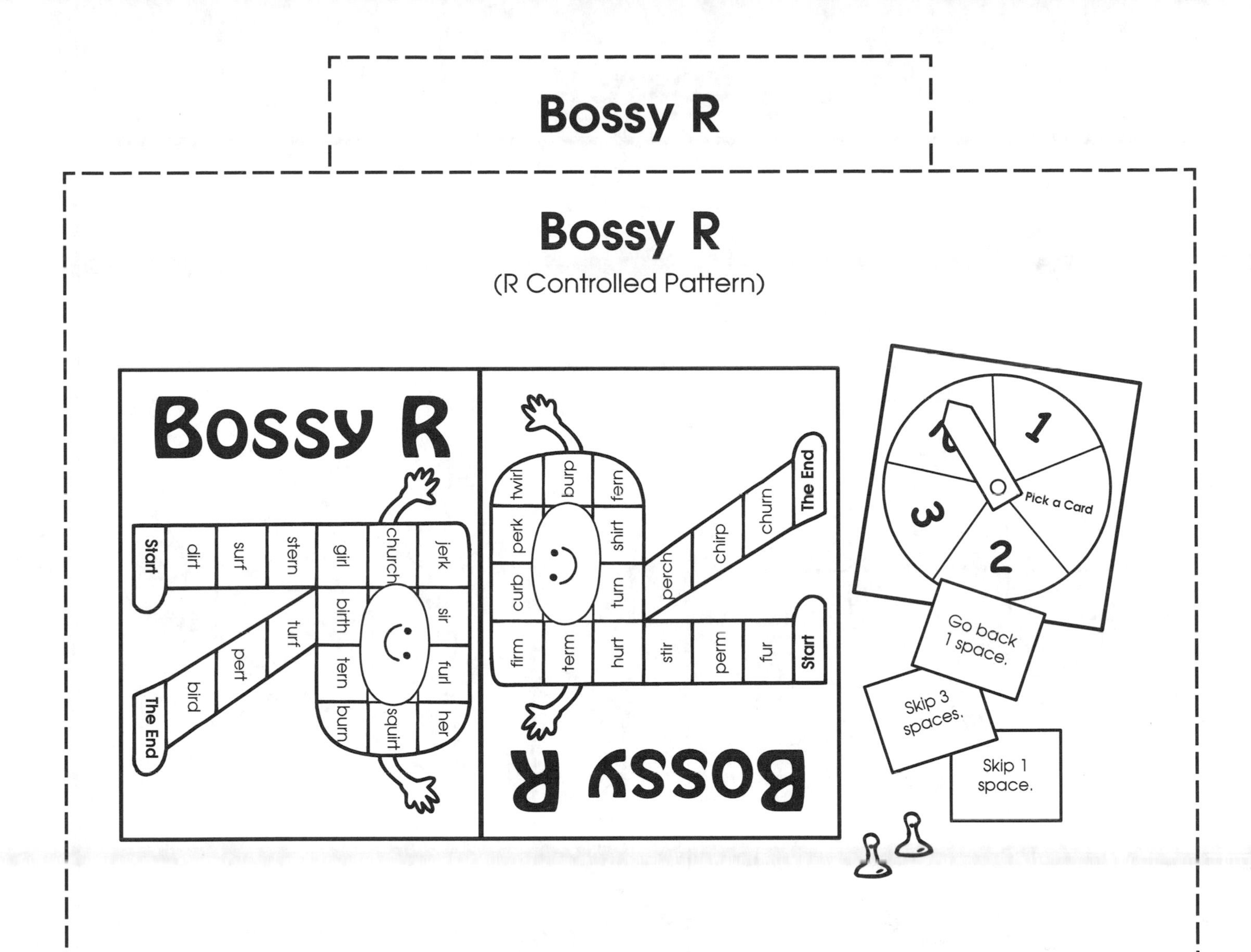

How to Play: 2 players may play. Set the game board and spinner in playing area. Shuffle and place the direction cards face down in a pile. Each player chooses a Bossy R to play. Each player takes a marker and places it on Start on his/her Bossy R. Each player in turn spins the spinner. If the spinner points to a number, player moves his/her marker that number of spaces. Player reads the word on the space. If the spinner points to Pick a Card, player must pick a direction card and follow the direction. The first player to reach The End is the winner.

How to Make: Duplicate the game board, spinner and wheel and direction cards. Duplicate the direction cards two times. Glue the game board on the inside of a file folder. Glue spinner, wheel and game cards on oak tag and cut out. Fasten spinner to wheel with a brass fastener. Cut out direction cards. Provide two markers. Store direction cards, spinner wheel, and markers in a clasp envelope. Glue envelope onto the back of the file folder. Duplicate the game directions, game illustration and game tab and cut. Glue directions and illustration to the front of the file folder. Glue game tab onto the file tab.

Bossy R

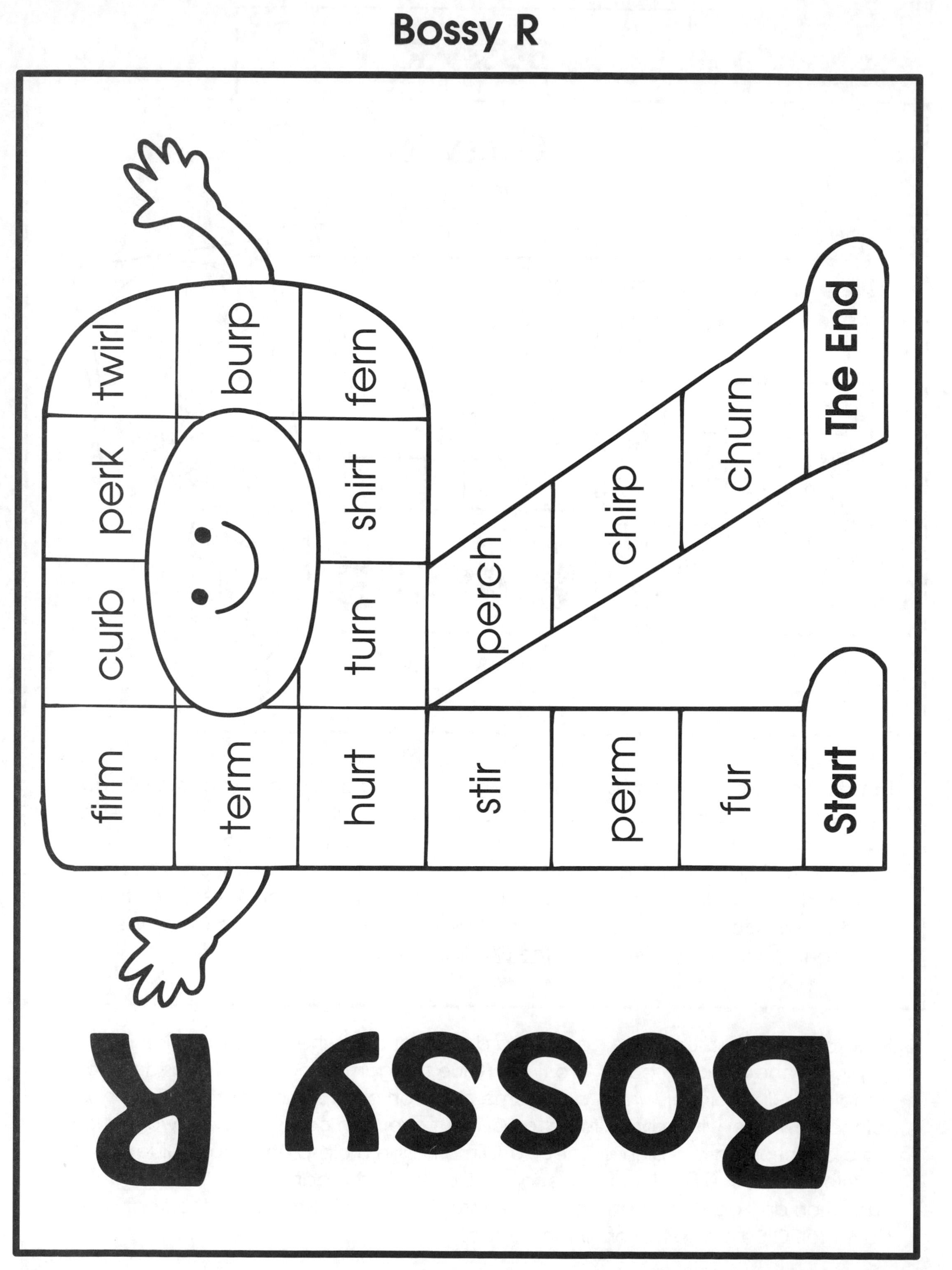
Bossy R
Start
fur
perm
stir
hurt
term
firm
curb
turn
perk
shirt
twirl
burp
fern
perch
chirp
churn
The End

Bossy R

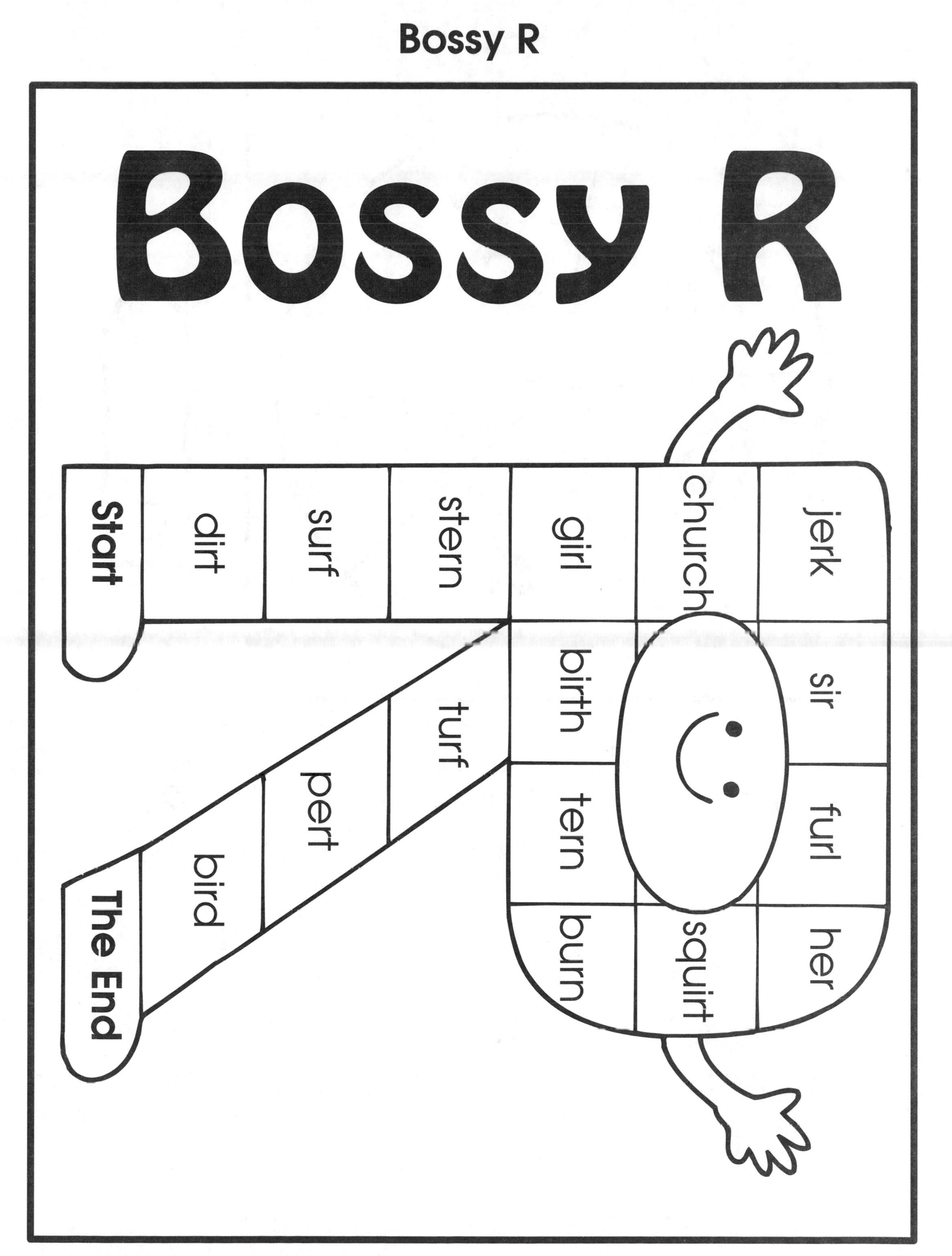

Bossy R
Start
dirt
surf
stern
girl
church
jerk
sir
birth
furl
tern
her
squirt
burn
turf
pert
bird
The End

Bossy R

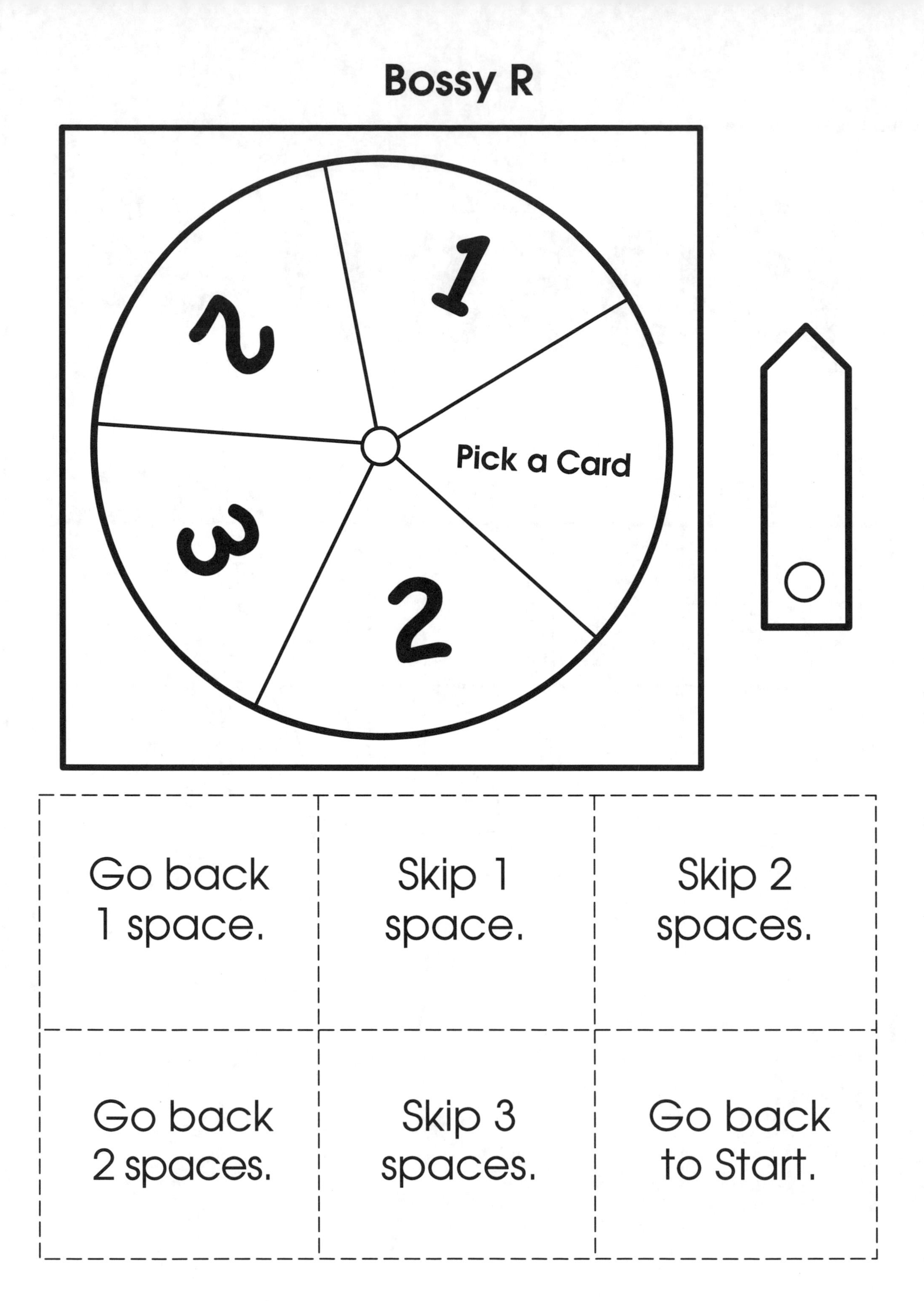

Duplicate direction cards two times. Provide two markers.

Sail Away!

The **ai** in **sail** and **ay** in **play** are **vowel teams**. **Two** vowels come together to make one vowel sound. The **y** in **ay** is a vowel. Both **ai** and the **ay** say the long **a** sound. Read the **ai** and **ay** words below.

ai	**ay**
tail **main**	**say** **pay**

Write the words with **ai** and **ay** on the boats that match. Read the words.

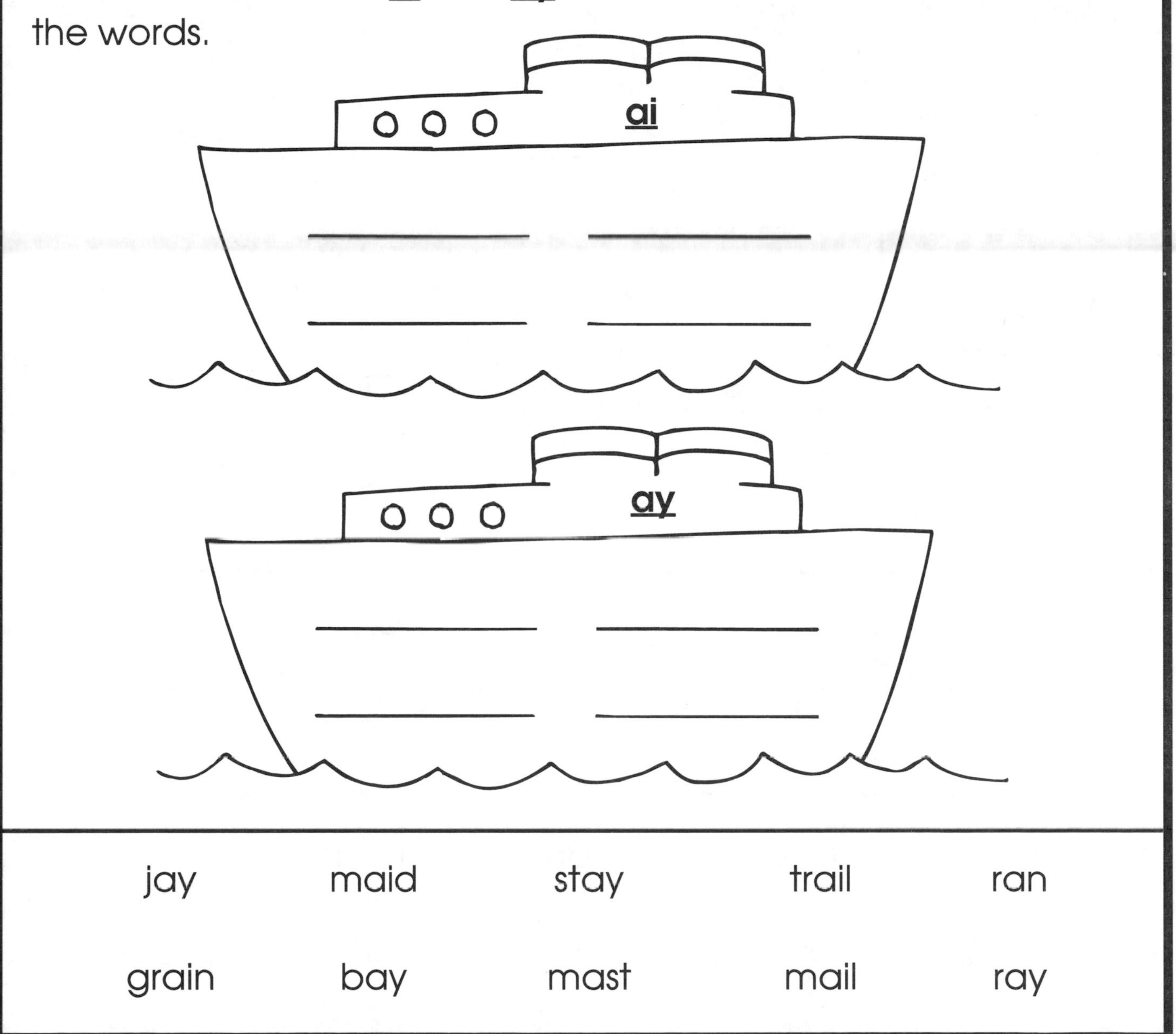

jay	maid	stay	trail	ran
grain	bay	mast	mail	ray

Jeep on the Road

The **ee** in **jeep** and the **oa** in **goat** are **vowel teams. Two** vowels come together to make **one** vowel sound. The **ee** in **jeep** says the long **e** sound. The **oa** in **goat** says the long **o** sound. Read the **ee** and **oa** words below.

ee	**oa**
bee keep	**boat soap**

Write the words with **ee** and **oa** on their roads. Read the words.

oak feet spot load peep

seed moan heel sent toad

Vowel Teams

Three cheers for **vowel teams**! Read the ai, ay, ee, and oa words on the cubs' shirts.

sail may see oak

Read each sentence and the **vowel team** words below. Write the correct word for the blank in each sentence.

1. The green ______________ hopped onto the log.
(sheep toad jay)

2. The Club will ______________ at my house to play.
(coat day meet)

3. Ann put the cups on the ______________ for Mom.
(tray mail load)

4. Mike saw a long snake cross the ______________.
(moan trail pay)

5. I like to ______________ on my back at the lake.
(float speed day)

6. Let's ______________ the ducks at the pond!
(road say feed)

Moon Book

The **oo** in **moon** and **oo** in **book** are **vowel teams**. **Two** vowels come together to make **one** vowel sound. The **oo** vowel teams have their own vowel sounds. Read the **oo** words below.

oo moon	**oo book**
cool room	**cook wood**

Cut and paste the words with **oo** as in **moon** and **oo** as in **book** on their page.

Tricky Seal

The vowel team **ea** can say the **long e** sound as in **seal**. Or it can say the **short e** sound as in **bread**. Read the **ea** words below.

ea **seal** **bead** **heat**

ea **bread** **head** **tread**

Color the word circles with **ea** as in **seal** green.
Color the word circles with **ea** as in **bread** red.

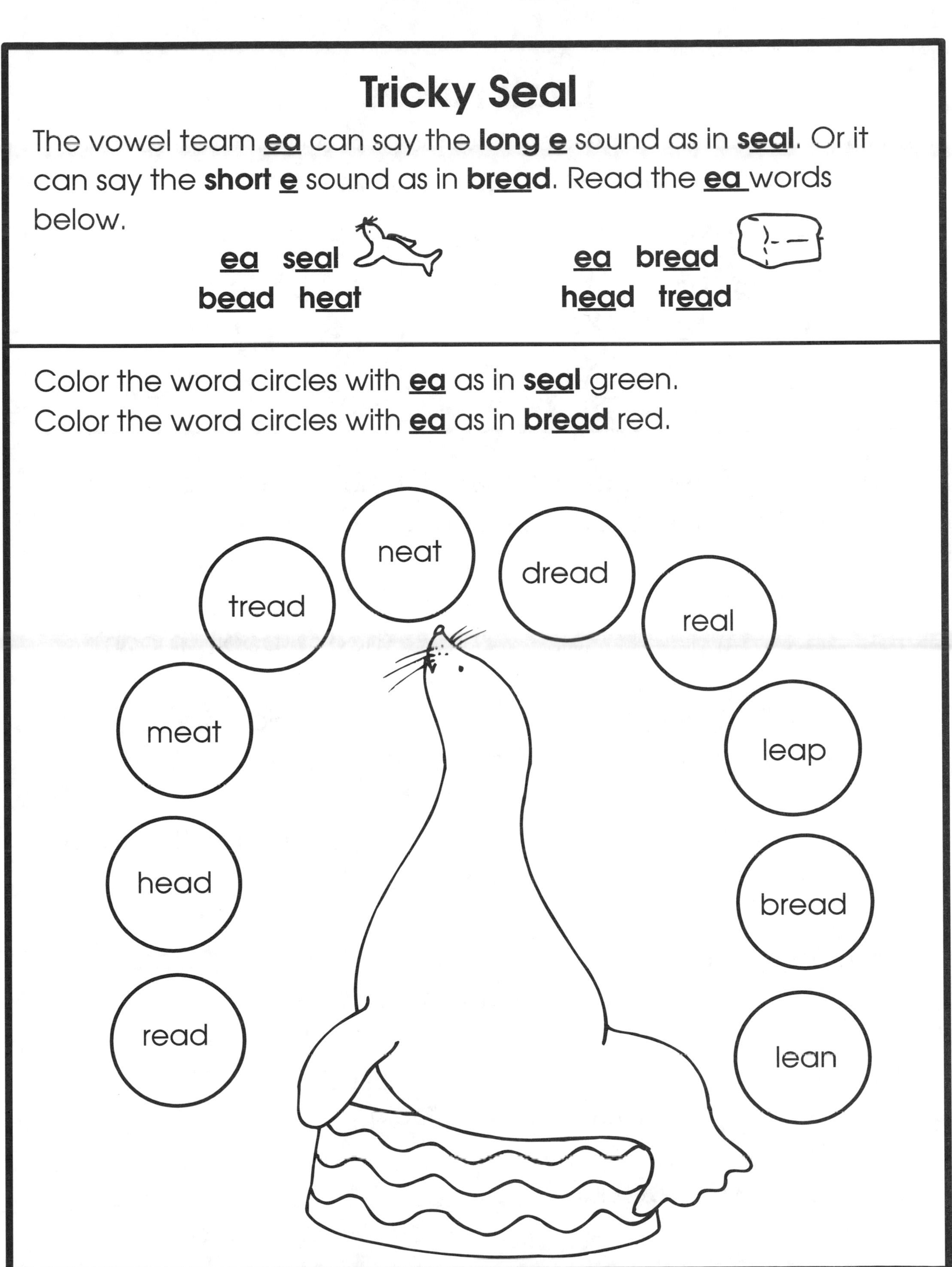

Look Alikes

The **vowel teams** below look alike but have their own vowel sounds. Read the word for each look alike.

oo oo
moon book

ea ea
seal bread

Read each sentence and the words below. Write the correct word on the blank for each sentence.

1. We will catch the fish with the ________________ .
(hook pool moon)

2. "Who will cut the ________________ ?" said Little Red Hen.
(beak wheat lead)

3. Stand on the ________________ to get the book!
(hook toot stool)

4. How long can you ________________ water?
(read tread neat)

5. Someone ________________ my lunch.
(room soon took)

6. Her room was nice and ________________ .
(neat read deal)

Twins

The **oi** in **oil** and **oy** in **boy** are **vowel teams**. **Two** vowels come together to make **one** vowel sound. The **y** in **oy** is a vowel. Both **oi** and the **oy** say the same sound. Read the **oi** and **oy** words below.

oi	**oy**
coil join	**boy joy**

Write the words with **oi** and **oy** on the twins. Read the words.

Roy soil toy boil seal

rain Troy oink soy coin

Haunted House

The **au** in **Paul** and **aw** in **saw** are **vowel teams. Two** vowels come together to make **one** vowel sound. The **w** in **aw** is a vowel. Both **au** and the **aw** say the same sound. Read the **au** and **aw** words below.

au	**aw**
Paul **haul**	**saw** **jaw**

Cut and paste the words with **au** and **aw** on the haunted house. Read the words.

haunt	raw	fault	paw	boy
soil	haul	crawl	vault	prawn

A Great Crew

The **ew** in **few** and **ew** in **blew** are **vowel teams**. **Two** vowels come together to make **one** vowel sound. The **w** in **ew** is a vowel. The **ew** vowel teams have their own sounds. Read the **ew** words below.

ew few **ew blew**

new hew **crew stew**

Cut and paste the words with **ew** on their boats. Read the words.

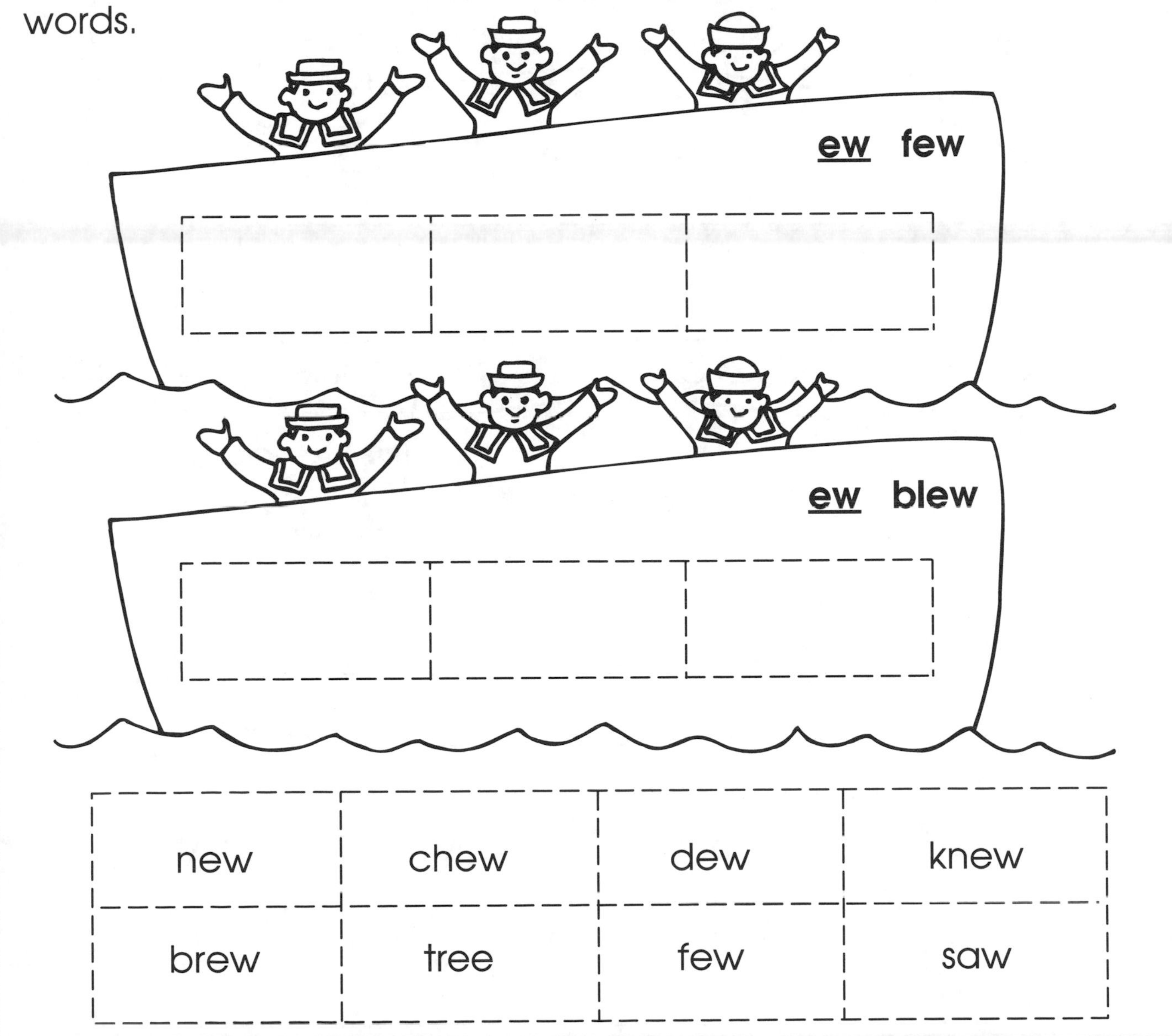

new	chew	dew	knew
brew	tree	few	saw

Down in the Sub

The **ow** in **down** and **ou** in **out** are **vowel teams**. **Two** vowels come together to make **one** vowel sound. The **ow** and **ou** say the same sound. Read the **ow** words below.

ow	**down**	**ou**	**out**
now	**how**	**loud**	**round**

Cut and paste the words with **ow** and **ou** on their subs. Read the words.

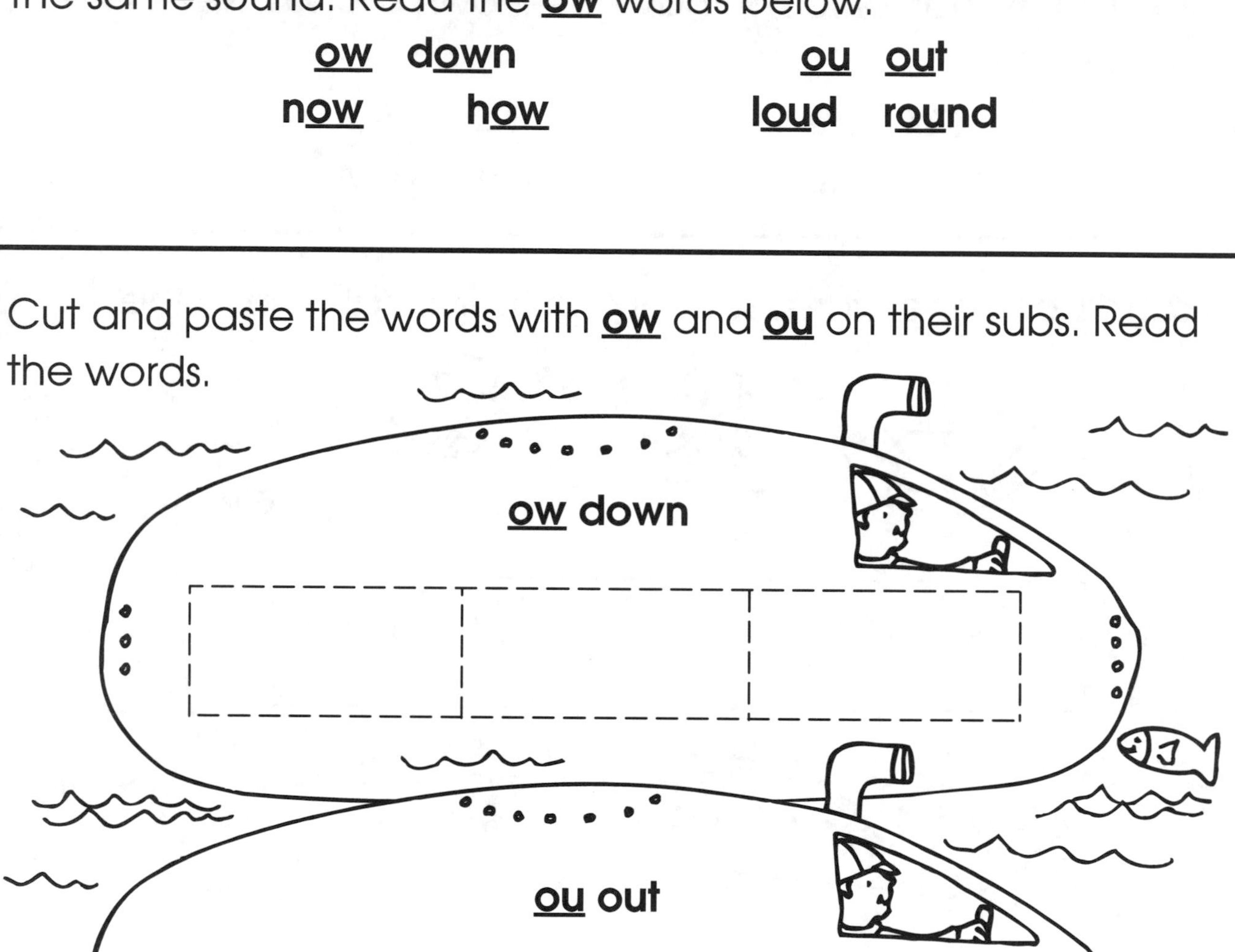

need	proud	cow	howl
cloud	brown	few	scout

Vowel Team Word Search

Find the oi, oy, aw, au, ew, and ow vowel team words in the Word Search below. Go across or down. Circle the words. Find 16 vowel team words. Read the words.

oi oy aw au ew ow ou

b	h	a	u	l	l	c	k	b	o	y
m	s	t	g	a	p	o	h	o	r	n
v	c	r	e	w	i	w	j	i	o	h
s	o	u	n	d	c	y	p	l	o	w
w	i	d	a	h	e	c	g	j	f	t
s	l	a	u	n	c	h	a	e	s	m
j	c	g	m	f	l	e	k	m	r	i
d	g	o	d	r	a	w	m	f	o	w
f	e	w	m	b	i	t	o	y	u	x
p	b	v	r	o	a	z	t	o	t	k
c	n	p	n	e	w	e	l	o	u	d

Words to Find: coil, boil, boy, toy, haul, launch, draw, law, cow, plow, loud, out, few, new, chew, crew

Road Race

Road Race

(Vowel Teams)

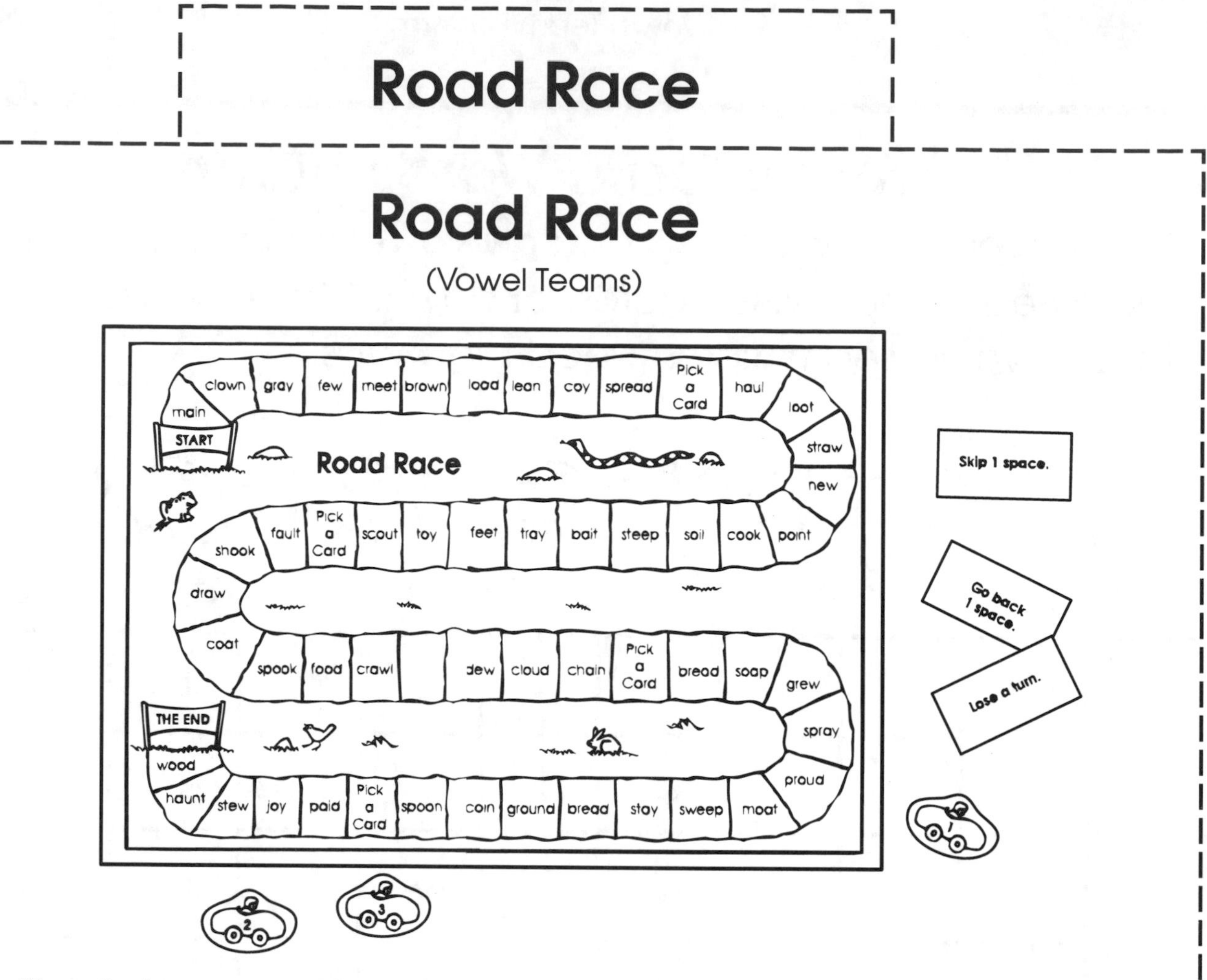

How to Play: 3 players may play. Set the game board in playing area. Shuffle and place the Direction cards face down in a pile. Each player takes a car marker and places it on Start. Each player in turn throws the die and moves his/her marker the number of spaces indicated on the die. Player reads the vowel team word on the space. If the player reads the word incorrectly, he/ she moves back one space. If a player lands on Pick a Card, he/ she picks a card from the pile and follows the direction. Discard the card. The first player to reach The End is the winner.

How to Make: Duplicate the game board and the direction cards and markers. Glue the game set-up on the inside of a file folder. Glue the direction cards and markers onto oak tag. Cut out the cards and markers. Provide a die. Store cards and markers in a clasp envelope. Glue envelope onto the back of the file folder. Duplicate the game directions, game illustration and game tab and cut. Glue directions and illustration to the front of the file folder. Glue game tab onto the file tab.

Road Race

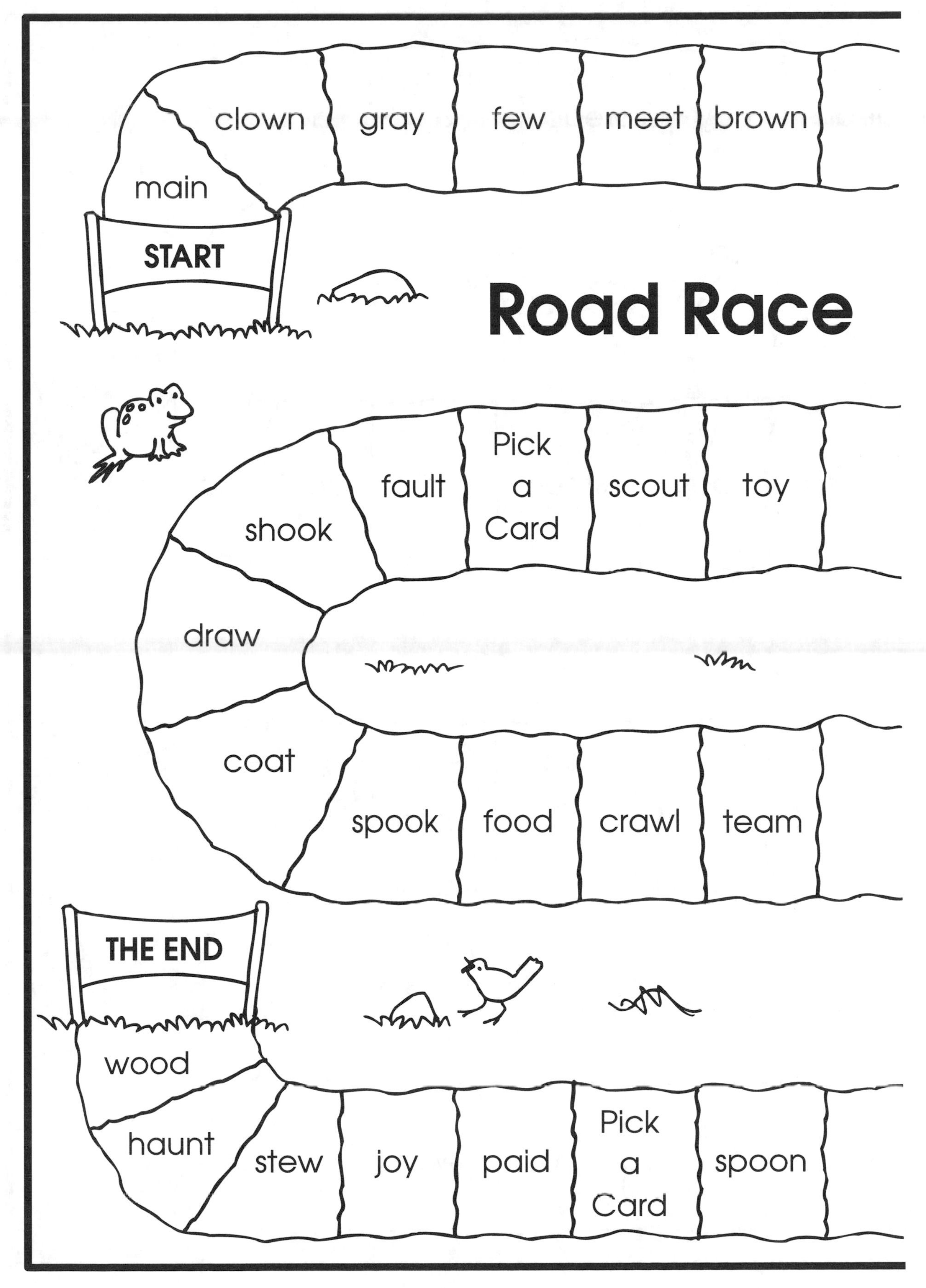

Provide a die.

Road Race

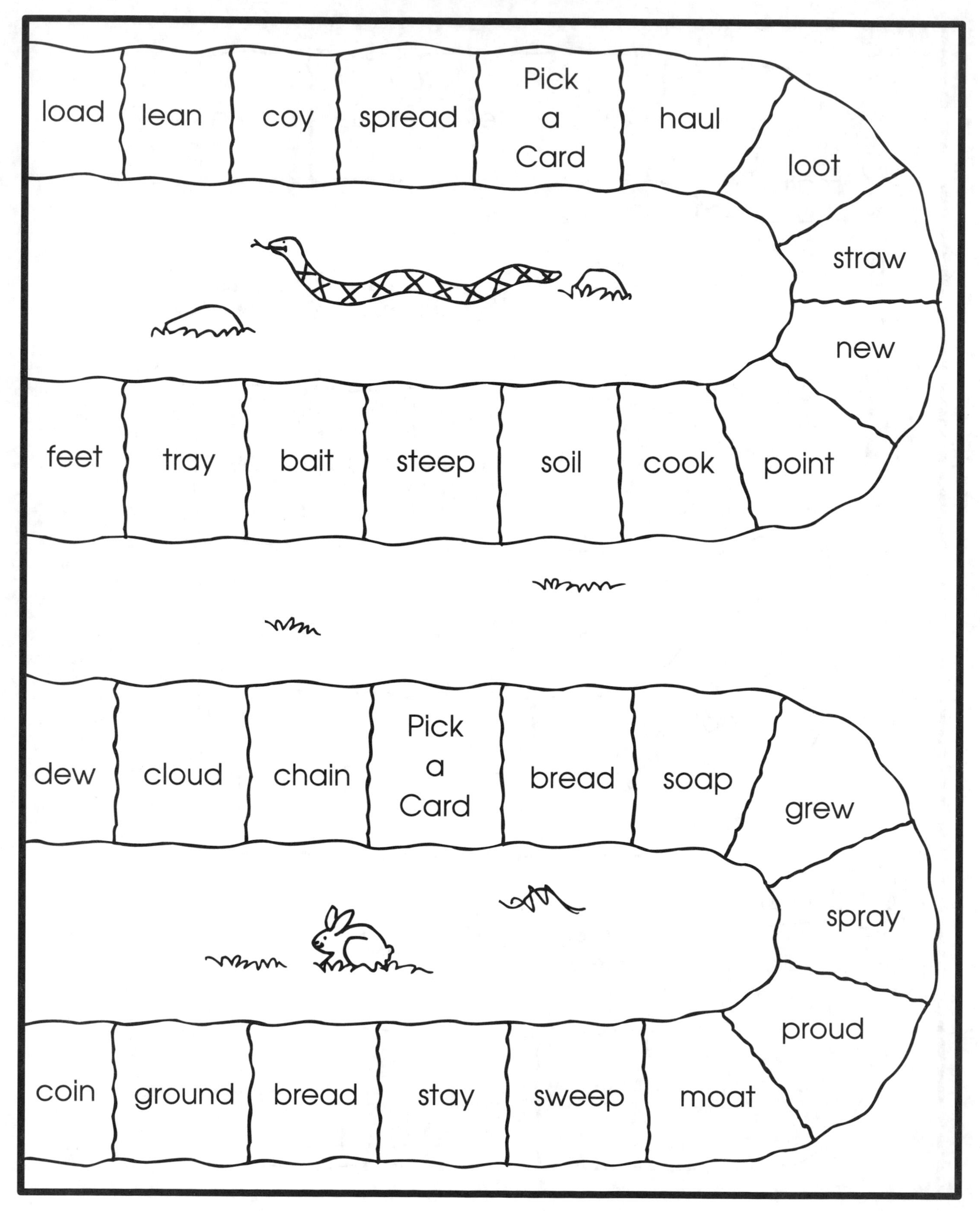
load
lean
coy
spread
Pick a Card
haul
loot
straw
new
point
cook
soil
steep
bait
tray
feet
dew
cloud
chain
Pick a Card
bread
soap
grew
spray
proud
moat
sweep
stay
bread
ground
coin

Road Race

Skip 1 space.	Go back 1 space.	Go back to Start.
Skip 1 space.	Go back 1 space.	Go back to Start.
Skip 1 space.	Go back 1 space.	Lose a turn.
Skip 2 spaces.	Go back 1 space.	Lose a turn.
Skip 2 spaces.	Go back 2 spaces.	Lose a turn.
Skip 3 spaces.	Go back 3 spaces.	Lose a turn.

1

2

3

A Little Puzzle

In the syllables **tle**, **zle**, **gle**, a **consonant** is followed by **le**. The **e** is silent. Read the **tle**, **zle**, and **gle** words below. The words are divided into syllables.

lit/tle **puz/zle** **wig/gle**

Cut and paste the **tle**, **zle**, or **gle** pattern to make words. Read the words.

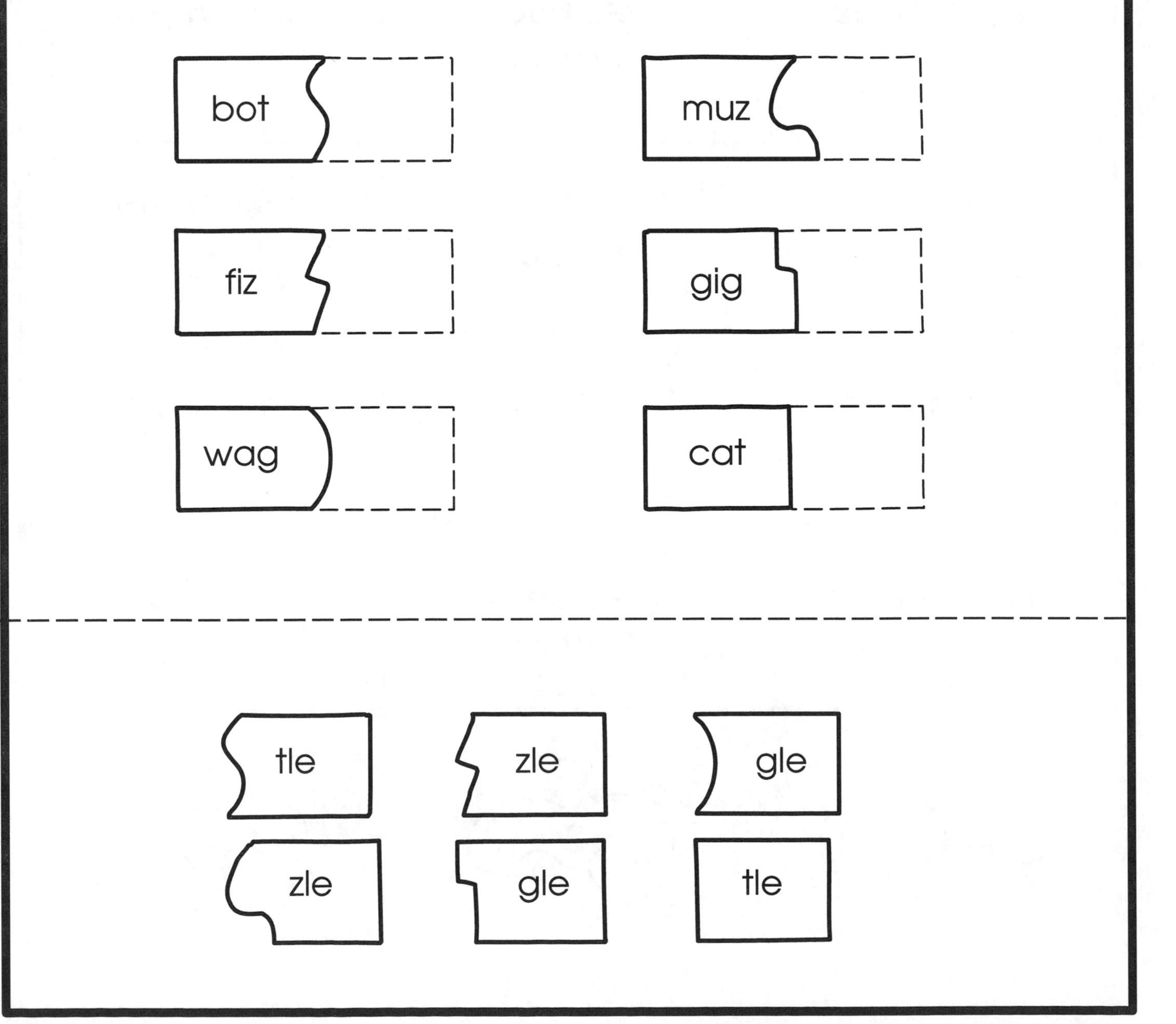

Fiddle Faddle

In the syllables **dle**, **fle**, **ple**, a **consonant** is followed by **le**. The **e** is silent. Read the **fle**, **dle**, and **ple** words below. The words are divided into syllables.

fid/dle **raf/fle** **ap/ple**

Write and add the **fle**, **dle**, or **ple** pattern to finish the words on the fiddles. Read the words.

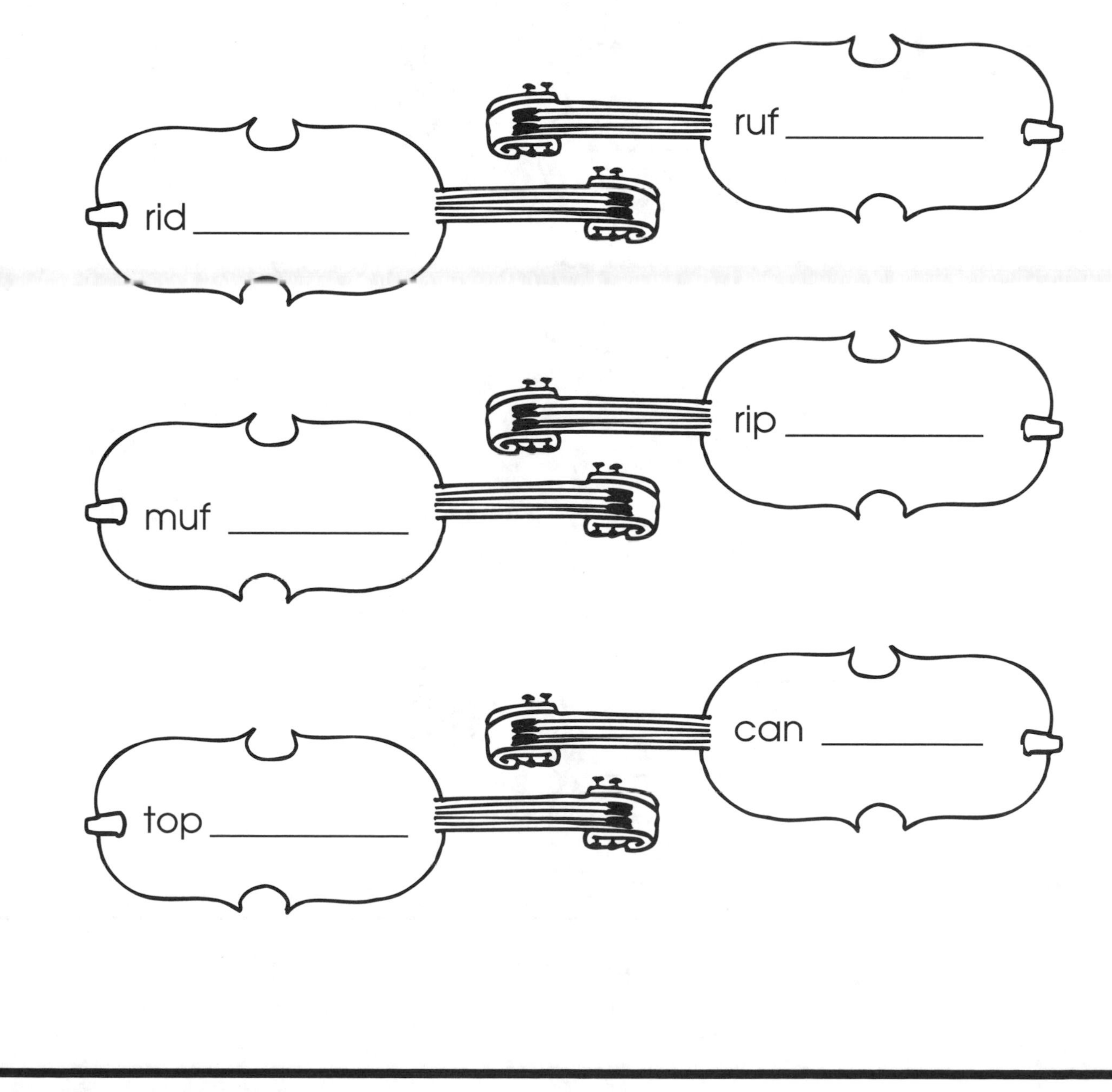

Bumble Bee

In the syllables **ble**, **cle**, **kle**, a **consonant** is followed by **le**. The **e** is silent. Read the **ble**, **cle**, and **kle** words below. The words are divided into syllables.

bum/ble **pop/si/cle** **krin/kle**

Write the **ble**, **cle**, and **kle** words on their hives. Read the words.

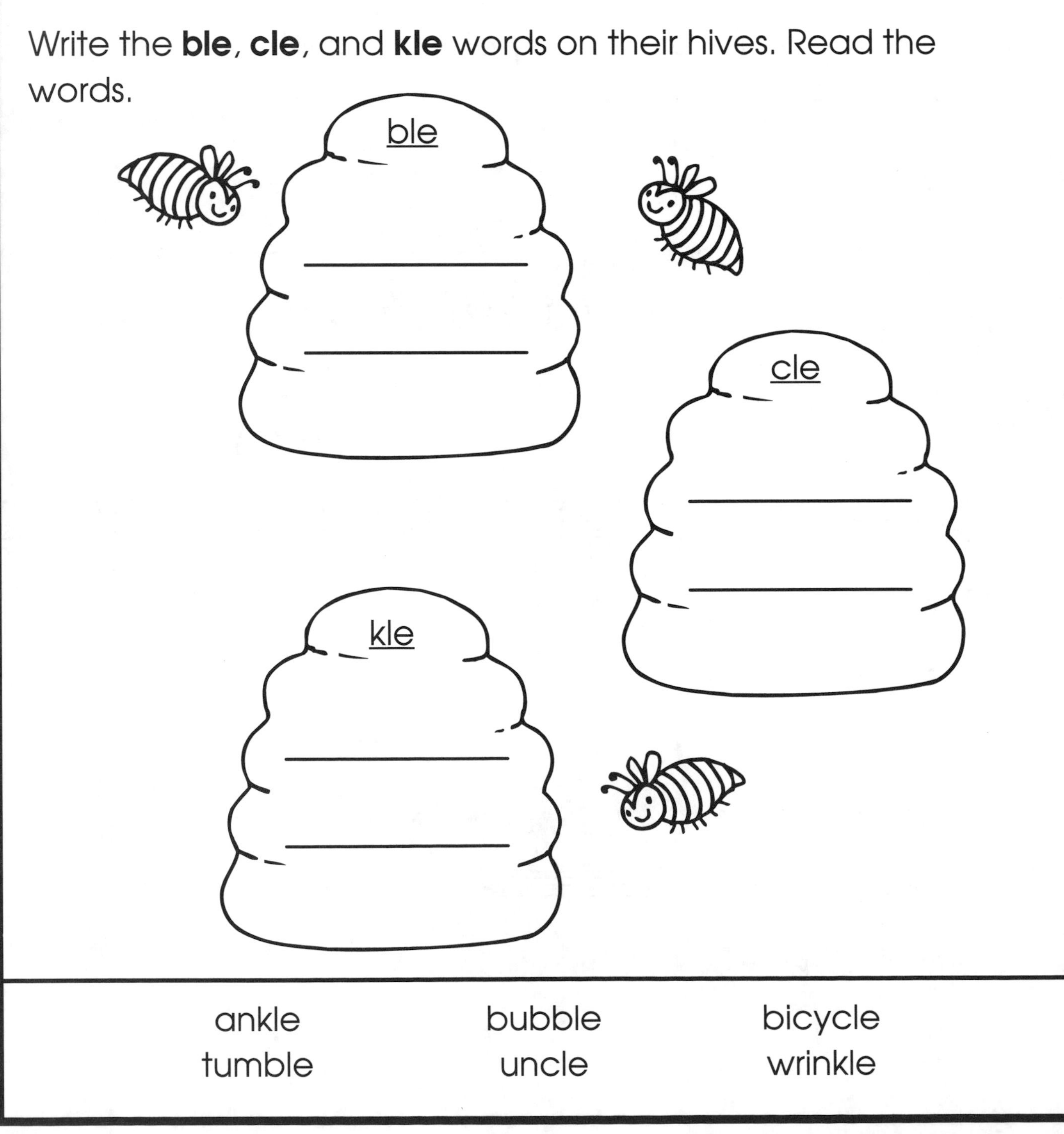

ankle	bubble	bicycle
tumble	uncle	wrinkle

Apples on the Tree

Apples on the Tree

(Consonant + le Pattern))

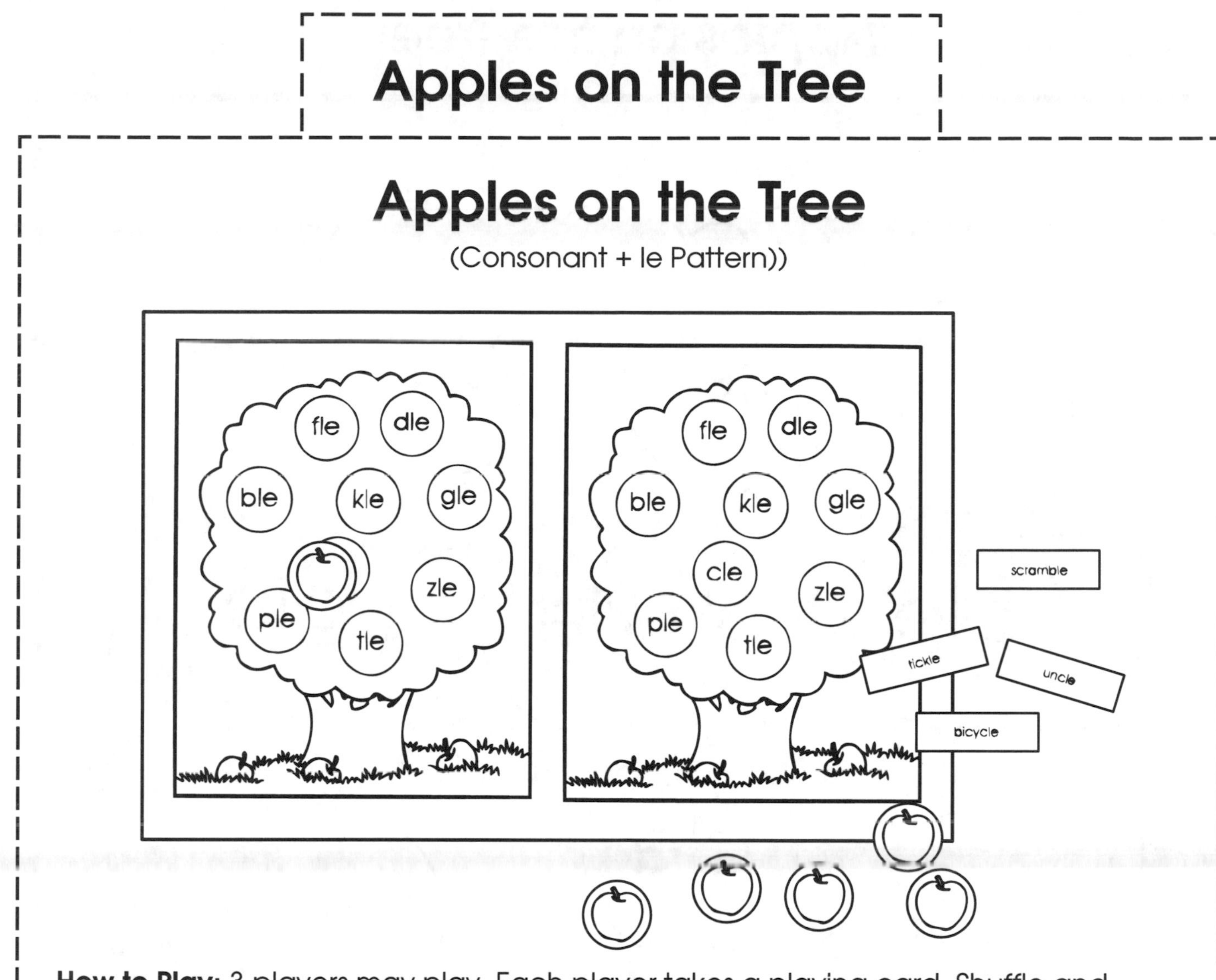

How to Play: 3 players may play. Each player takes a playing card. Shuffle and place the word cards face down in playing area. Place apples in the playing area face up. Each player in turn takes a word card and reads the word on it and names the consonant + le pattern, i.e. ble, ple, tle, etc. If correctly read and identified, player places an apple over that pattern on the player's tree. If the word is incorrectly read, player must place the word card back in the pile. Used cards are discarded. If there are no more pattern circles for a word card picked, player places the card back into the pile. The first player to cover all the patterns with apples is the winner.

How to Make: Duplicate the game playing card three times. Trim and glue onto oak tag. Duplicate the consonant + le word cards. Glue onto oak tag and cut out. Duplicate the apple circles and glue onto oak tag. Cut out. Store playing cards, word cards, and apples in a clasp envelope. Duplicate the game directions and cut. Glue onto the front of the clasp envelope.

Apples on the Tree

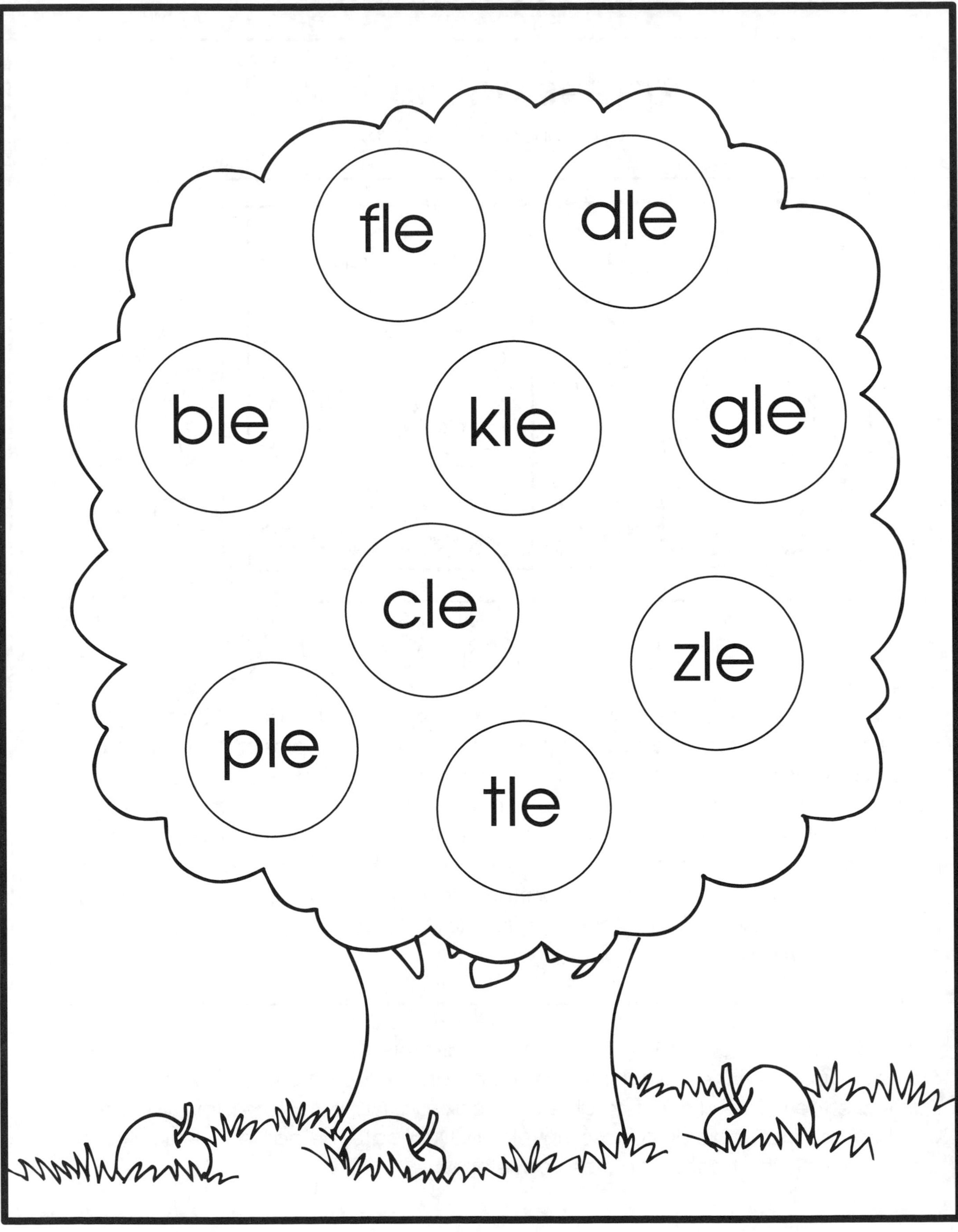

Duplicate three times.

Apples on the Tree

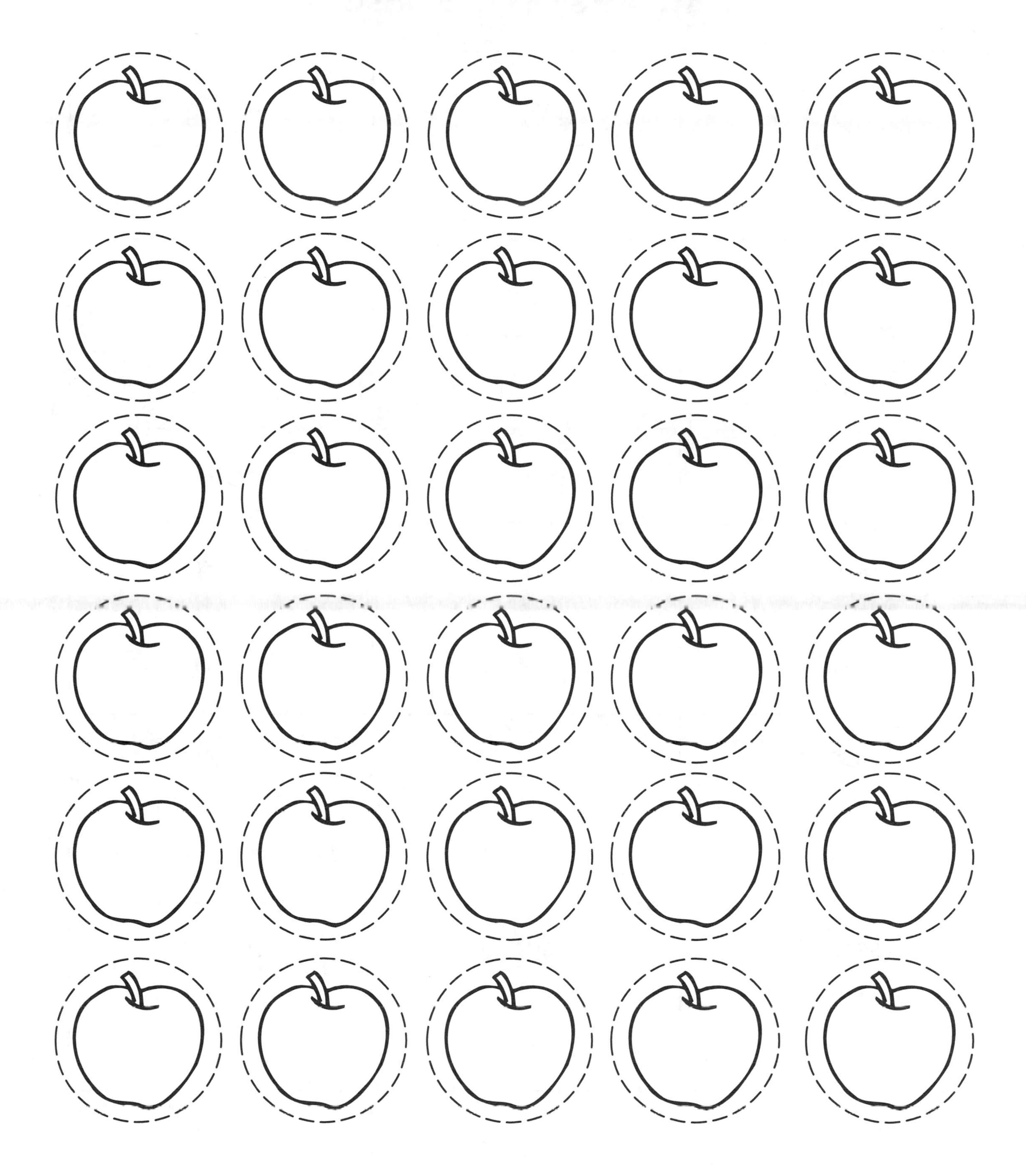

Duplicate three times.

Apples on the Tree

bubble	bumble	scramble
wobble	uncle	bicycle
icicle	popsicle	buckle
tickle	ankle	wrinkle
fiddle	puddle	bundle
handle	ruffle	muffle
duffle	raffle	giggle
dangle	tangle	jungle
ripple	simple	topple
sample	settle	cattle
battle	whittle	puzzle
sizzle	dazzle	muzzle